COLOR STA

AND

COLOR NOMENCLATURE

RIDGWAY

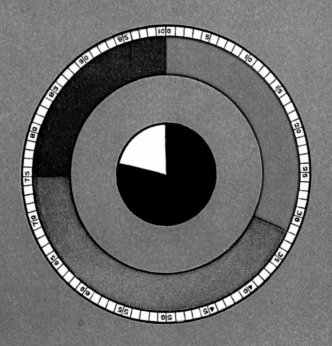

FIFTY-THREE COLORED PLATES

ELEVEN HUNDRED AND FIFTEEN NAMED COLORS

COLOR STANDARDS

AND

COLOR NOMENCLATURE

— — —.— —

BY

ROBERT RIDGWAY, M. S., C. M. Z. S., ETC.

Curator of the Division of Birds, United States
National Museum.

——.——

With Fifty-three Colored Plates

and

Eleven Hundred and Fifteen Named Colors.

——.——

WASHINGTON, D. C.
1912.
Published by the Author.

PRESS OF
A. HOEN & COMPANY
BALTIMORE, MD

PREFACE

THE motive of this work is THE STANDARDIZATION OF COLORS AND COLOR NAMES.

The terminology of Science, the Arts, and various Industries has been a most important factor in the development of their present high efficiency. Measurements, weights, mathematical and chemical formulæ, and terms which clearly designate practically every variation of form and structure have long been standardized ; but the nomenclature of colors remains vague and, for practical purposes, meaningless, thereby seriously impeding progress in almost every branch of industry and research.

Many works on the subject of color have been published, but most of them are purely technical, and pertain to the physics of color, the painter's needs, or to some particular art or industry alone, or in other ways are unsuited for the use of the zoologist, the botanist, the pathologist, or the mineralogist ; and the comparatively few works on color intended specially for naturalists have all failed to meet the requirements, either because of an insufficient number of color samples, lack of names or other means of easy identification or designation, or faulty selection and classification of the colors chosen for illustration. More than twenty years ago the author of the present work attempted to supply the deficiency by the publication of a book* containing 186 samples of named

---

*A | Nomenclature of Colors | for Naturalists, | and | Compendium of Useful Knowledge | for Ornithologists. | By | Robert Ridgway, | Curator, Department of Birds, United States National Museum. | With ten colored plates and seven plates | of outline illustrations. | Boston : | Little, Brown, and Company. | 1886. | (12mo., pp. 129, pls. 17.)

The subject of color and color nomenclature discussed on pages 15-58. Plates i-x, inclusive, represent 186 named colors, hand-painted (stencilled).

colors, but the effort was successful only to the extent that it was an improvement on its predecessors; and, although still the standard of color nomenclature among zoologists and many other naturalists, it nevertheless is seriously defective in the altogether inadequate number of colors represented, and in their unscientific arrangement. Fully realizing his failure, the author, some two or three years later, began to devise plans, gather materials, and acquire special knowledge of the subject, in the hope that he might some day be able to prepare a new work which would fully meet the needs of all who have use for it. Unfortunately, his time has been so fully occupied with other matters that progress has necessarily been slow; but after more than twenty years of sporadic effort it has at last been completed.

Acknowledgments are due to so many friends for helpful suggestions that it is hardly possible to name them all, or to specify the extent or kind of help which each has rendered; but special mention should be made of Mr. LEWIS E. JEWELL, of Johns Hopkins University; Dr. R. M. STRONG, of the University of Chicago; Prof. W. J. SPILLMAN, of the U. S. Department of Agriculture; Mr. WILLIAMS WELCH, of the U. S. Signal Service; Mr. MILTON BRADLEY, of Springfield, Mass.; Dr. P. G. NUTTING, of the U. S. Bureau of Standards; Mr. P. L. RICKER, of the Bureau of Plant Industry, U. S. Department of Agriculture; and Mr. J. L. RIDGWAY, of the U. S. Geological Survey. The late Professor S. P. LANGLEY, then Secretary of the Smithsonian Institution, was good enough to take a kindly interest in this undertaking and gave the author assistance for which he is glad to make acknowledgment. More than to all others, however, is the author deeply indebted to Mr. JOHN E. THAYER, of Lancaster, Mass., and Señor Don JOSÉ C. ZELEDÓN, of San José, Costa Rica, for aid so indispensible that without it the work could not have been completed.

To Dr. G. GRÜBLER & Co., of Leipzig, Germany, the author is under obligations for the gift of a nearly complete set of their celebrated coal-tar dyes, which have proven quite necessary to the work, especially in the coloring of the Maxwell disks on which the color scheme is based.

The reproduction of the plates has been a difficult matter, involving not only expensive experimentation, but more than three years of unremitting labor. Vastly different from the ordinary lines of commercial color work, the correct copying of each one of the 1115 colors of the original plates developed many perplexing and often discouraging problems, which were finally solved through Mr. A. B. HOEN'S expert knowledge of chemistry and pigments; the skill, industry, and patience of the firm's head colorist, Mr. FRANK PORTUGAL, and the personal interest of both these gentlemen. It is, therefore, with the greatest pleasure that the author's grateful acknowledgment is made to the firm of A. HOEN & COMPANY for the satisfactory manner in which they have fulfilled their contract.

CONTENTS

PROLOGUE

As stated in the Preface, the purpose of this work is the standardization of colors and color nomenclature, so that naturalists or others who may have occasion to write or speak of colors may do so with the certainty that there need be no question as to what particular tint, shade, or degree of grayness, of any color or hue is meant. Therefore, it is unnecessary to treat of the subject from any other point of view ; it will be sufficient to say that this work is based on a thorough study of the subject from every standpoint, and that practically all authoritative works on the subject of color have been carefully consulted.*

PLAN.—The scientific arrangement of colors in this work is based essentially on the suggestions of Professor J. H. Pillsbury for a scheme of color standards,† which have also been the basis of several other efforts toward the same end, as the plates in Milton Bradley's "Elementary Color" and educational colored papers, Prang's charts of standard colors, Klinkseick and Valette's "Code des Couleurs," etc.; but while all these present a scientifically arranged color-scheme and more or less adequate

---

*Titles of several books on the subject which are especially recommended to the lay student of chromatology are given at the end of this text.

†See *Science*, June 9, 1893, and *Nature*, Vol. LII, No. 1347, Aug. 22, 1895, pp. 390–392.

number of colors they all fail to supply a ready or
convenient means of identifying and designating the
colors—the principal utility of a work of this kind. It is
in the latter respect that the present work is believed to
meet, more nearly than any other at least, this essential
requirement, and in this consists whatever originality
may be claimed for it.

The "key" to the classification or arrangement here-
with presented is, of course, the solar spectrum, with its
six fundamental colors and intermediate hues, augmented
by the series of hues connecting violet with red, which
the spectrum fails to show. If, with the red-violets and
violet-reds thus added to the spectrum hues, the band
forming this scale be joined end to end a circle is formed
in which there is continuously a gradual change of hue,
step by step, from red through orange-red and red-orange
to orange ; orange through yellow-orange and orange-
yellow to yellow; yellow through green-yellow and yellow-
green to green; green through blue-green and green-blue
to blue; blue through violet-blue and blue-violet to violet;
and violet through red-violet and violet-red to red—the
starting-point—with intermediate connecting hues. In
the solar spectrum, both prismatic and grating, but
especially the former, the spaces between the adjoining
distinct colors are very unequal; therefore for the present
purpose an ideal scale must be constructed, so that an
approximately equal number of equally distinct connecting hues shall be shown. Distinctions of hue appreciable
to the normal eye are so very numerous* that the
criterion of convenience or practicability must determine
the number of segments into which the ideal chromatic
scale or circle may be divided in order to best serve the
purpose in view. Careful experiment seems to have

---

* According to Aubert more than 1000 hues are distinguishable in the spectrum,
though among them all the hues betweeen violet and red are wanting.

demonstrated that thirty-six is the practicable limit, and accordingly that number has been adopted.* If the number of intermediate hues were equal in all cases there would, in this scheme, be five between each two adjacent fundamental colors of the spectrum; but a greater number of recognizably distinct hues is obviously necessary in some cases than in others; for example, spectrum orange is decidedly nearer in hue to red than to yellow, and therefore the number of intermediates required on each side of the orange is different, being in the proportion of four for the red-orange series to five for the orange-yellow, and similarly six are required for the violet-red series, while four suffice for the blue-violet hues.

There is no known means by which we can measure the proportion of two or more *pigments* in any given mixture, "because color-effect cannot be measured by the pint of mixed paint or the ounce of dry pigment;"† but, fortunately, we have a very exact method, in the color-wheel and Maxwell disks, by which the relative proportions of two or more *colors* in any mixture may be precisely measured. This method has been used in the painting of every one of the 1115 colors of the present work, by means of one disk to represent each one of the thirty-six colors (both pure and "broken"), together with a black, a white, and a neutral gray disk, the last being a match in color to the gray resulting from the mixture of red, green and violet on the color-wheel;‡ the neutral gray disk, however, being used only for the making of disks for the broken series of colors (′, ″, ‴, ‴′, and ‴″) and for the scale of neutral grays (Plate

---

*That is to say, the practical limit for pictorial representation of the colors in their various modifications.

†Milton Bradley: Elementary Color, p. 18.

‡See colored figure on frontispiece.

LIII.) These colored disks are slit on one side from center to circumference, and therefore by interlocking two or more they may be adjusted so that either occupies any desired percentage of the whole area, which may be very precisely determined by a scale of 100 segments shown on the outer edge of a larger disk on which the colored disks are superimposed. When connected with the color-wheel and adjusted as may be desired, and then rapidly revolved, the two or more distinct colors resolve themselves into a single uniform composite color, whose elements are shown, in their relative proportion, by the scale surrounding the disks.*

The scales (both horizontal and vertical) of the present work are all prepared directly from definite color-wheel formulæ, based on carefully calculated curves; the thirty-six pure spectrum hues, represented

---

*See the colored figure on the frontispiece of this work, which clearly illustrates this method of color measurement. Larger disks of spectrum red, green, and violet are interlocked and adjusted so that they present, respectively, 32, 42, and 26 per cent. of the circumference; superimposed on these is a single smaller disk of neutral gray, and on this two still smaller disks of black and white, the former occupying 79, the latter 21, per cent. of the area. The result of this combination of colors, when the disks are rapidly revolved, is that the entire surface becomes a uniform neutral gray precisely like the middle disk, which blends so completely with the color inside and outside its limits that no trace of division can be detected. Hence, neutral gray equals a combination of red 32, green 42, and violet 26 per cent., and also equals a combination of black 79 and white 21 per cent. As further illustrating the point, it may be mentioned that not only does the above-mentioned combination of the three primary colors equal neutral gray but so also does the combination of any color ("secondary" or "tertiary" as well as primary) with its complementary, though the darkness or lightness of the gray varies somewhat, as the following table shows:

SPECTRUM COLOR.		COMPLEMENTARY COLOR.		EQUIVALENT GRAY.	
Name.	Per Cent.	Per Cent.	Composition.	Black.	White.
Red	44	56	Blue 41 + Green 59.	72.5	27.5
Orange............	28.5	71.5	Blue 51.5 + Green 48.5.	69	31
Yellow	33	67	Blue 60.5 + Violet 39.5.	64	36
Green	51	49	Red 57.5 + Violet 42.5.	73	27
Blue	64	36	Yellow 82 + Orange 18.	62	37
Violet.............	62.5	37.5	Yellow 69 + Green 31.	61.5	38.5

by the middle horizontal line of color-squares on Plates
I-XII (together with an equal number of intermediates
represented by blank spaces), requiring a separate curve
and consequently different relative proportions of the
two component colors for each series of hues—that is,
the series from red to orange, orange to yellow, yellow
to green, green to blue, blue to violet, and violet to red,
respectively; but the progressive increments of white in
the scales of tints, black in those of shades, and neutral
gray in the several series of broken colors are exactly
the same in every case. The first series of Plates (I-XII)
shows the pure, full spectrum colors and intermediate
hues (middle horizontal line, nos. 1-72),* each with its
vertical scale of tints (upward, a-g) and shades (downward, h-n), the increments of white for the tints being
9.5, 22.5, and 45 per cent., respectively, those of black
in the shades being 45, 70.5, and 87.5 per cent. The
remaining Plates show these same thirty-six colors or
hues in exactly the same order and similarly modified
(vertically) by precisely the same progressive increments of white (upward) and black (downward), but
all the colors are dulled by admixture of neutral gray;
the first series (1'-72', Plates XIII–XXVI) containing 32
per cent. of neutral gray, the second (1"-72", Plates
XXVII–XXXVIII) 58 per cent., the third (1'''-72''',
Plates XXXIX–XLIV) 77 per cent., and the fourth (1''''-
72'''', Plates XLV–L) 90 per cent. The last three
Plates (LI-LIII) show the six spectrum colors† (also
purple, the intermediate between violet and red) still
further dulled by admixture of 95.5 per cent. of neutral

---

*The number is doubled so that every other one represents an intermediate hue
not shown in color.

†Owing to the circumstance that spectrum orange does not, at least when mixed
with gray, fairly represent a medium hue between red and orange, being much
nearer the former, a hue much near to yellow (yellow-orange, No. 15) has been
selected.

gray, these being in reality colored grays; to which are
added a scale of neutral gray and one of carbon gray, the
former being the gray resulting from mixture of the three
primary colors (red 32, green 42, violet 26 per cent.,
which in relative darkness equals black 79.5, white 20.5
per cent.); the latter being the gray produced by mixture of lamp black and Chinese white, and the scale a
reproduction of that in the author's first "Nomenclature
of Colors" (1886, Plate II, nos. 2-10). It should be
emphasized that in all cases except the scale of carbon
grays, only the disks representing the middle horizontal
series of colors (both pure and broken) have been used, in
combination with a black and a white disk, respectively,
to make the colors of the vertical scales of tints and
shades.

The coloring of a satisfactory set of disks to represent the thirty-six pure spectrum colors and hues was a
matter of extreme difficulty, many hundreds having been
painted and discarded before the desired result was
achieved. Several serious problems were involved, the
matter of change of hue through chemical reaction of the
combined pigments or dyes* (especially the latter) being
almost as troublesome as that of securing the proper
degree of difference between each adjoining pair of hues.
The method by which satisfactory results were finally
secured was as follows: First, six disks were colored
to represent each of the fundamental spectrum colors,

*For satisfactory color-wheel work it is necessary to discard practically all the
so-called artists' colors, as being much too dull to even approximately represent the
colors of the spectrum, and to substitute carefully selected aniline or coal-tar dyes,
of which, fortunately, there is a very large number of remarkable purity of hue.
Indeed, the work of most color-physicists is vitiated by their use of such crude colors
as vermilion, carmine, scarlet-lake, chrome yellow, emerald green, Prussian blue, etc.
(For a list of dyes and pigments used in preparing the Maxwell disks representing
the thirty-six colors of the chromatic scale, see pages 26, 27.)

according to the author's conception of them.* These six disks were then placed against a suitable background (a neutral gray), in spectrum sequence, with wide intervals for the accommodation of connecting series of disks, which were then colored so as to represent an apparently even transition from one to the other. When this very difficult task had been done as well as the eye alone could judge, each intermediate was then measured on the color-wheel and the relative proportions (in percentages) of its two component colors recorded. After this had been done for all the intermedite hues each series (the red-orange, orange-yellow, yellow-green, green-blue, blue-violet, and violet-red) was taken separately and a curve constructed on cross-section paper from the recorded ratios. These curves were found to be in all cases more or less irregular or unsymmetrical, but nevertheless were sufficiently near correct to serve as a basis for a symmetrical curve; and after the points out of

*In fixing the exact position or wave-length of the spectrum colors considerable latitude is allowable, the element of "personal equation"—that is, difference in the conception of different persons as to just where the reddest red, greenest green, etc., are located, accounting for the considerable disagreement among chromatologists as to the wave-lengths. The following table, showing the average, mean, and extreme wave-length of each of the spectrum colors as given by nine or more authorities together with those of the present work (as determined by Dr. P. G. Nutting, Associate Physicist of the U. S. Bureau of Standards) is of interest in this connection :

	This work.	Average of 9-12 authorities.	Extremes of 9-12 authorities.	Mean of 9-12 authorities.
Red	644	6770	6440–7028	6734 (10)
Orange	598 ± 2	6074	5892–6300	6096 (9)
Yellow.................	577 ± 1	5786	5640–5850	5745 (10)
Green......	520 ± 10	5235	5050–5335	5193 (11)
Blue...	473 ± 3	4738	4520–4861	4680 (12)
Violet	410	4176	4050–4330	4190 (10)

From this table it will be seen that the red of this work is appreciably more orange than that of others, the orange slightly more yellowish, and the violet a little less bluish than the average; but the author is assured by Dr. Nutting that these standards are exceptionally accurate.

proper line were suitably relocated the two component colors were correspondingly readjusted on the color-wheel and each faulty disk corrected (or a new one painted) until it exactly matched the required combination. The scales representing the tints and shades of each color, and also the gray or broken colors were similarly determined by corrected curves.*

By the method adopted of running each of the thirty-six spectrum hues through a scale of tints and shades, and repeating the combination through several series modified by increasing increments of neutral gray, practically the entire possible range of color variation is covered,† rendering it an easy matter to locate in the plates, either among the colors actually shown or in an intermediate space, any color which it is desired to match; and where short distinctive names have not been found (their place being, tentatively, supplied by compound names), as, necessarily, must often be the case, any color or intermediate between any two colors, either as to hue, tint, or shade, may be readily designated by the very simple system of symbols (numerals and letters) employed.‡

In order to designate any color for which a satisfactory name cannot be found, or one not represented on the plates, it is only necessary to proceed as follows: Suppose the color in question is nearest 1 on Plate I; say, for example, is intermediate in hue between 1 (spectrum red) and 3 (scarlet-red), or in other words if represented in color its position would be in the uncol-

---

*The percentages are given in tables on pages 23 and 25.

†That is to say, theoretically. Unfortunately it seems to be beyond the colorists' skill to reproduce true shades of the pure colors, all showing a more or less decided admixture of gray, resulting in a series of broken or dull shades. (See pages 23 and 24.)

‡Although only 1115 different colors are actually shown on the plates the system is really equivalent to the presentation of considerably more than 4000 distinguishable and designatable colors.

ored space designated as no. 2 ; and in tone between the full color (middle horizontal line) and tint *b*. Its designation, therefore, is *2a*. Exactly the same method applies to any of the other blank spaces, as well as to the colors themselves, except that in case of the broken colors the "primes" (′, ″, ‴, ⁗, or ′′′′′) are to be affixed to the hue number. First locate the *hue*, designated by number, then the *tone*, designated by lower case letter, the full, pure colors of the middle horizontal row being designated by number alone.

COLOR NAMES.—While it is true that the naming of colors as usually employed has so little to do with the purely technical aspects of chromatology or color-physics that, as Von Bezold remarks[*] "we are in reality dealing with the peculiarities of language," it is equally true that a collection of color standards designed expressly for the purpose of identifying and designating particular colors can best attain this object by the use of a carefully selected nomenclature. In other words, the prime necessity is to standardize both colors and color names, by elimination of the element of "personal equation" in the matter. In no other way can agreement be reached as to the distinction between "violet" and "purple," two color names quite generally used interchangeably or synonymously but in reality belonging to quite distinct hues, or that any other color name can be definitely fixed. Various methods of handling the matter of color in zoological and botanical descriptions, etc., by the avoidance of color names and substitution therefor of symbols, numerals, or mechanical contrivances (as color-wheel and spectrum analyses, color-spheres, etc.) have been devised but all have been found impracticable or unsatisfactory. The author has taken the trouble to get an expression of opinion in this matter from many

[*]The Theory of Color (American edition, 1876), p. 99.

naturalists and others, and the preference for color-
names very greatly predominates; consequently, when-
ever it has been possible to find a name which seems
suitable for any color in this work it has been done,
leaving as few as possible unnamed, and for these some
other means must be devised for their designation. (See
page 8). The selection of appropriate names for the
colors depicted on the Plates has been in some cases a
matter of considerable difficulty. With regard to certain
ones it may appear that the names adopted are not entirely satisfactory; but, to forestall such criticism, it may
be explained that the purpose of these Plates is not to
show the color of the particular objects or substances
which the names suggest, but to provide appropriate, or
at least approximately appropriate, names for the colors
which it has seemed desirable to represent. In other
words, certain colors are selected for illustration, for
which names must be provided; and when names that
are exclusively pertinent or otherwise entirely satisfactory are not at hand, they must be looked up or invented. It should also be borne in mind that almost any
object or substance varies more or less in color; and that
therefore if the "orange," "lemon," "chestnut" or
"lilac" of the Plates does not exactly match in color the
particular orange, lemon, chestnut or lilac which one
may compare it with, it may (in fact does) correspond
with other specimens. Without standardization, even
if arbitrary, color nomenclature must, necessarily, remain
in its present condition of absolute chaos. Even the
standard pigments are not constant in color, practically
every one of them being subject to more or less variation
in hue or tone, different samples from the same manufacturer sometimes varying to the extent of several tones
or hues of the present work; indeed, in every case where
two or more samples of the same color have been com-

pared it has been found that no two are exactly alike, the difference often being very great. For example: Of five samples of "vandyke brown" only two are approximately similar, each of the other three being widely different, not only from one another but from the other two, one being a blackish brown, another reddish brown, the third a yellowish orange-brown. Of eleven samples of "olive" no two are closely similar, the color ranging from a shade of dull (grayish) blue-green to orange-brown, dark brownish gray, and light yellowish olive; and the same or nearly the same degree of variation is seen in absolutely every color examined, showing very clearly the utter worthlessness of color names unless fixed or standardized.

In order to obtain as many color names as possible for standardization it has been necessary to draw from all available sources. Several thousand samples of named colors have therefore been collected, and for convenience of reference and comparison gummed to card catalogue cards, with the name, source, and other data thereon. These include the colors from many standard works, among them Werner's "Nomenclature of Colours" (Syme's edition, 1821), Hay's "Nomenclature of Colours" (1846), Ridgway's "Nomenclature of Colors" (1886), Saccardo's "Chromataxia" (1891), Mathews' "Chart of Correct Colors of Flowers" (American Florist, 1891), Willson and Calkins' "Familiar Colors," Oberthur and Dauthenay's "Repertoire des Couleurs" (1905), Leidel's "Hints on Tints" (1893), "Lefévré's Matieres Colorantes Artificiales" (1896), the Standard Dictionary chart of "typical colors," the educational colored papers of Milton Bradley and Prang, and many others; and besides these practically all of the artists' oil, water, and dry colors, manufactured by Winsor and Newton, F. Schoenfeld and Co., Charles Roberson and Co.,

George Rowney and Co., Madderton and Co., R. Acker-
mann and Co., Bourgeois, Binant, Chenal, Le Franc,
Devoe, Raynolds, Osborne, Bradley, Hatfield and others;
also the coal-tar or aniline dyes of Dr. G. Grübler & Co.,
Continental Color and Chemical Co., and Henry Heil
Chemical Co., and the well known Diamond Dyes;
chromo-lithographic inks, embroidery silks, etc., etc.

The material from which to select suitable color
names was greatly augmented, almost at the last moment,
from two sources, as follows: (1) A very large collection
of color-samples (unfortunately mostly unnamed) collected and mounted on cards by Mr. Frederick A. Wampole, a talented young artist, to whom was delegated,
by a Committee of the American Mycological Society,
the task of preparing a nomenclature of colors based
upon spectroscopic determinations, but which, unfortunately, the untimely death of Mr. Wampole pre-
vented from progressing beyond the accumulation of this
collection.   For the use of this material I am indebted
to the courtesy of Dr. Frederick V Coville, Botanist of
the U. S. Department of Agriculture, and Mr. P. L.
Ricker, Assistant Botanist, Bureau of Plant Industry,
in the same Department.   (2) A splendid collection of
colored Japanese silks, taffetas, velvets, and other dress
goods, kindly sent me by Mr. C. H. Hospital, of the silk
department of the firm of Woodward and Lothrop,
Washington, D. C.   The very large number of colors
represented in this collection are all named and have
afforded a considerable number of the names adopted in
the present work.

For obvious reasons it has, of course, been necessary
to ignore many trade names, through which the popular
nomenclature of colors has become involved in really
chaotic confusion rendered more confounded by the con-
tinual coinage of new names, many of them synonymous

and most of them vague and variable in their application. Most of them are invented, apparently without care or judgment, by the dyer or manufacturer of fabrics, and are as capricious in their meaning as in their origin; for example : Such fanciful names as "zulu," "serpent green," "baby blue," "new old rose," "London smoke," etc., and such nonsensical names as "ashes of roses" and "elephant's breath." An inspection of the sample books of manufacturers of fancy goods (such as embroidery silks and crewels, ribbons, velvets, and other dress- and upholstery-goods) is sufficient not only to illustrate the above observations, but to show also the absolute want of system or classification and the general unavailability of these trade names for adoption in a practical color nomenclature. This is very unfortunate, since many of these trade names have the merit of brevity and euphony and lack only the quality of stability

It has been difficult for the author to decide whether the standards of his original "Nomenclature of Colors" (1886) should be retained in the present work. Some of them are admittedly wrong (indeed, certain ones are not as they were intended to be); besides, owing to the method of reproducing the originals (hand stenciling) there is considerable variation in different copies of the book, one or more reprints, necessitating new mixtures of pigments, adding to this lack of uniformity.* Many persons, however, have urged the retention of the old standards, on the ground that they have been used by so many zoologists and botanists in their writings during the last twenty-five years that they have become estab-

*In the present work the possibility of variation between different copies is wholly eliminated by a very different process of reproduction. Each color, for the entire edition, is painted uniformly on large sheets of paper from a single mixture of pigments, these sheets being then cut into the small squares which represent the colors on the plates.

lished through common usage. This very important
consideration has induced the author to retain such of
the old standards as can be matched in the present work,
even though some of them do not agree strictly with
either his own or the usual conception of the colors in
question. An asterisk (*) preceding a color name in-
dicates that the name in question is adopted from the
older work, the variation between different copies of the
work requiring the selection, in the new one, of a color representing as nearly as possible an average of the former.

In any systematically arranged scheme, unless the
number of colors shown is practically unlimited, it will,
necessarily, be impossible to find represented thereon a
certain proportion of colors comprised among even a
very limited number selected at random, or only rough-
ly classified. Hence many (thirty-six, or more than
five per cent.) of the colors shown in the old "Nomenclature of Colors" fall into the blank intervals of the
present work, being intermediate either in hue or tone,
or chroma, sometimes all. It is necessary of course to
provide some means for the correlation of these with the
present scheme, which is done by the list on page 41,
where the position of each is shown.

The question of giving representations of metallic
colors in this work was at one time considered; but the
idea was abandoned for the reason that these are in
reality only ordinary colors reflected from a metallic or
burnished surface, or appearing as if so reflected; the
actual hue is precisely the same, though often change-
able according to angle of impact of the light rays, and
relative position of the eye, this changeableness being
sometimes due to interference.* Colors again vary,
without actual difference of hue, in regard to quality of
texture or surface; that is to say, the color may be quite

*See Rood, Modern Chromatics, pages 50-52.

lustreless, appearing on a dull, sometimes velvety surface, while again it may be more or less glossy, even to the degree of appearing as if varnished. To deal with these variations, however, requires simply the use of suitable adjectives. For example: To indicate a color which has no lustre or brightness, the adjective matt (or mat) may be used, in preference to *dull*, which implies reduction in purity or chroma; other adjectives, appropriate in special cases, being velvety, glossy, burnished metallic, matt-metallic, etc.

COLOR TERMS.—No other person has presented so forcibly the urgent need for reform in popular nomenclature nor stated so clearly and concisely its shortcomings and the simple remedy, as Mr. Milton Bradley, from one of whose educational pamphlets on the subject* the following is quoted: ''The list of words now employed to express qualities or degrees of color is very small, in fact a half dozen comprise the more common terms, and these are pressed into service on all occasions, and in such varied relations that they not only fail to express anything definite but constantly contradict themselves . . . Tint, Hue and Shade are employed so loosely by the public generally, even by those people who claim to use English correctly, that neither word has a very definite meaning, although each is capable of being as accurately used as any other word in our every day vocabulary'' . . .

Certainly one would expect that men of learning, at least, would employ the broader color terms correctly; but some of the highest autorities on color-physics habitually use them interchangeably, as if they were quite synonymous; and even the dictionaries, with few exceptions, give incorrect or ''hazy'' definitions of these

---

*Some criticisms of Popular Color Definitions and Suggestions for a better Color Nomenclature. Milton Bradley Co., Springfield, Mass. (Small pamphlet of 15 pages).

terms. It is not strictly correct to say a "dark tint" or "light shade" of any color, because a *tint* implies a color *paler* than the full color, while a shade means exactly the opposite; and to say an "orange shade (or tint) of red," a "greenish shade (or tint) of blue," a "bluish shade (or tint) of violet," etc., is an absurdity, for the term *hue*, which specifically and alone refers to relative position in the spectrum scale, without reference to lightness or darkness, is the only one which can correctly be used in such cases.

Indeed the standardization of color terms is almost if not quite as important, in the interest of educational progress, as that of the colors themselves and their names; therefore, to make easy a clear understanding of the specific meaning of each, the following definitions are given:—

Color.—The term of widest application, being the only one which can be used to cover the entire range of chromatic manifestation; that is to say, the spectrum colors (together with those between violet and red, not shown in the spectrum) with all their innumerable variations of luminosity, mixture, etc. In a more restricted sense, applied to the six distinct spectrum colors (red, orange, yellow, green, blue, and violet), which are sometimes distinguished as *fundamental colors* or *spectrum colors*.

Hue.—While often used interchangeably or synonymously with color, the term *hue* is more properly restricted by special application to those lying between any contiguous pair of spectrum colors (also between violet and purple and between purple and red); as an orange *hue* (not shade or tint, as so often incorrectly said) of red; a yellow *hue* of orange; a greenish *hue* of yellow, a bluish *hue* of green; a violet *hue* of blue, etc.

Tint.—Any color (pure or broken) weakened by high illumination or (in the case of pigments) by admixture of white, or (in the case of dyes or washes) by excess of aqueous or other liquid medium ; as, a deep, medium, light, pale or delicate (pallid) *tint* of red.   The term cannot correctly be used in any other sense.

Shade.—Any color (pure or broken) darkened by shadow or (in the case of pigments) by admixture of black ; exactly the opposite of *tint*; as a medium, dark, or very dark (dusky) *shade* of red.

Tone.—"Each step in a color scale is a tone of that color."*   The term tone cannot, however, be properly applied to a step in the spectrum scale, in which each contiguous pair of the six distinct spectrum or "fundamental" *colors* are connected by *hues*.   Hence *tone*† is exclusively applicable to the steps in a scale of a single color or hue, comprising the full color (in the center) and graduated tints and shades leading off therefrom in opposite directions ; or of neutral gray similarly graduated in tone from the darkest shade to the palest tint.   Each one of the colored blocks in the vertical scales of the plates in this work represents a separate tone of that color.

Scale.—A linear series of colors showing a gradual transition from one to another, or a similar series of tones of one color.   The first is a *chromatic scale*‡ (or scale of colors and hues) and in the plates of this work is represented by each horizontal series; the second is a

---

*Milton Bradley: Elementary Color, p. 25.

†Exception has been taken in a recent work ("A Color Notation," by A. H. Munsell) to the use of the term tone in this connection, on the ground that its proper use belongs to music, and the term *value* is substituted.   The same line of reasoning would, however, certainly require the discarding of *chromatic scale* as a term of music nomenclature, since its derivation is clearly from color (chroma).   Furthermore, the word "value" is even more elastic in its application than tone, and, all things considered, the present writer, at least, fails to see that any improvement is made by the proposed change.

‡The term *chromatic scale* has unfortunately been appropriated for a very different use (in music) ; nevertheless it is strictly correct in the present sense while in the other it is not, though firmly established by long usage.   The term *spectrum scale* is not adequate, as a substitute, because the spectrum series of colors is incomplete through absence of the hues connecting violet with red, which are necessary to show the full scale of pure colors and hues.

tone scale, on the plates running vertically, growing from the full color, in the center, to a pale tint (at the top) and a dark shade (at the bottom). For clearer comprehension of these two distinct scales, each plate of this work may be compared to a sheet of woven fabric; the chromatic scale (horizontal) representing the warp, the luminosity or tone scale (vertical) the woof. A third kind of color scale is represented by adding progressive increments of neutral gray to any color. This is shown by the several series of Plates, of which the first (Plates I-XII, with colors numbered 1-71) represents each step in the spectrum scale unmixed with gray, followed by five other series in which the same colors* are shown dulled by gradually increasing increments of neutral gray, the first (Plates XIII-XXVI, colors 1'-71') containing 32 per cent., the second (Plates XXVII-XXXVIII, colors 1"-71") 58 per cent., the third (Plates XXXIX-XLIV, colors 1'''-69''') 77 per cent., the fourth (Plates XLV-L, colors 1''''-69'''') 90 per cent., and the fifth (Plates LI-LIII, colors 1''''', 15''''', 23''''', 35''''', 49''''', 59''''' and 67''''') 95.5 per cent. of gray, the last being in reality colored grays. Finally scales are shown (on Plate LIII) of neutral gray (in which all trace of color is wanting), and of carbon gray, a simple mixture of lamp-black and chinese white. It is not easy to find a suitable name for these scales of reduced or "broken" colors, but they may, for present convenience, be termed *reduced* or *broken scales*.

Full Color.—A color corresponding in intensity with its manifestation in the solar spectrum.

---

*The distinctions of color or hue diminishing in proportion to the increased admixture of gray, each alternate color or hue, with its scale (vertical) of tones, is omitted from the third and fourth series; while in the fifth the color differentiation is so greatly reduced that only the six spectrum colors (dulled by admixture of 95.5 per cent. of neutral gray), together with purple (the intermediate between violet and red) are given; a yellow orange hue being substituted for spectrum orange because it is more exactly intermediate in hue between red and yellow.

Pure Color.—A color corresponding in purity with (or, in the case of material colors, closely approximating to) one of the spectrum colors.

Broken Color.—Any one of the spectrum colors or hues dulled or reduced in purity by admixture (in any proportion) of neutral gray, or varying relative proportions of both black and white; also produced by admixture of certain spectrum colors, as red with green, orange with blue, yellow with violet, etc. These broken colors are far more numerous in Nature than the pure spectrum colors, and include the almost infinite variations of brown, russet, citrine, olive, drab, etc. They are often called dull or neutral colors.

Fundamental Colors.—The six psychologically distinct colors of the solar spectrum; Red, Orange, Yellow, Green, Blue and Violet.

Primary Colors.—Theoretically, any of the spectrum colors which cannot be made by mixture of two other colors. According to the generally accepted Young-Helmholtz theory, the primary colors are red, green, and violet; orange and yellow resulting from a mixture of red and green, and blue from a mixture of green and violet. There is considerable difference of opinion, however, as to this question, and further investigation of the subject seems to be required; at any rate, authorities fail to explain why red may be exactly reproduced (except as to the degree of luminosity) by a mixture of orange and violet, exactly as yellow results from mixture of red and green or blue from green or violet, green being, in fact, the only spectrum color that cannot be made by mixture of other colors.*

*J. J. Müller found that a mixture of the orange and violet rays of the spectrum produced a whitish red (Rood, "Modern Chromatics," p. 129). The author of the present work, without being at the time aware of this, produced an absolutely pure red (but of reduced intensity) by mixture of either orange and violet (orange 63.5, violet 36.5 per cent.=red 85+white 15 per cent.), or from orange and the violet-red which is complementary to green (violet-red 51, orange 49 per cent.), the latter equaling red 89+white 11 per cent; the mixtures being made on a color wheel with Maxwell disks representing the pure colors of the present work. The red resulting from either of these mixtures on the color-wheel is far purer than the blue resulting from mixture of green and violet, and incomparably more so that the yellow resulting from mixture of either red and green or orange and green. Consequently, if the same results would come from mixing orange and violet light, it is difficult to understand how red can be a primary color *according to the accepted definition.*

Chroma. — Degree of freedom from white light; purity, intensity or fullness of color.

Luminosity. — Degree of brightness or clearness. The relative luminosity of the spectrum colors is as follows: [Yellow (brightest)?], orange yellow; orange; greenish-yellow, yellow-green, and green ; orange-red ; red and blue (equal); violet-blue, blue-violet, violet.*

Warm Colors. — The colors nearer the red end of the spectrum or those of longer wave-lengths (red, orange, and yellow, and connecting hues) "and combinations in which they predominate."†

Cool, or Cold, Colors. — The colors nearer the violet end of the spectrum or those of shorter wave-length, especially blue and green-blue. "But it is, perhaps, questionable whether green and violet may be termed either warm or cool."

Complementary Color. — "As white light is the sum of all color, if we take from white light a given color the remaining color is the complement of the given color." When any two colors or hues which when combined in proper proportion on the color-wheel produce, by rotation, neutral gray, these two colors each represent the complementary of the other.

Constants of Color. — The constants of color are numbers which measure (1) the wave-length, (2) the chroma, and (3) the luminosity.

In addition to the terms defined above there are many others, for which the reader is referred to the chapter on "Color Definitions" on pages 23-30 of Milton Bradley's excellent and most useful book "Elementary Color."

---

*Rood. Modern Chromatics, p. 34.

With the single exception of Vanderpoel (Color Problems, p. 28, plates 3, 4, where yellow is given first in order of luminosity) all authorities on color-physics that I have been able to consult very singularly ignore yellow entirely in their treatment of the subject of luminosity.

†All quotations here are from Milton Bradley's "Elementary Color," except where otherwise noted.

TABLE OF PERCENTAGES OF COMPONENT COLORS IN THE
CONNECTING HUES OF THE CHROMATIC SCALE.

The following table shows the relative percentages, in color-wheel measurement, of the two components in each of the hues connecting adjacent pairs of the six spectrum colors as represented on the original Plates of this work; together with an equal number of exact intermediates (not shown on the Plates), the latter in lower-case type and not indicated by symbols.

Number.	Color.	Red.	Orange.	Yellow.	Green.	Blue.	Violet.	Wavelength.[1]
1	Red	100	....	....	....	....	....	644
2	....	90	10	....	....	....	....	
3	O-R	80	20	....	....	....		
4	....	70	30	....				
5	OO-R	60	40	....				
6	....	50	50	....				
7	R-O	40	60	....				
8	....	30	70	....				
9	OR-O	20	80	....			....	
10	....	10	90	....		....	....	
11	Orange	....	100	....		....	.. ..	598
12	....	....	96	4		....	....	
13	OY-O	... .	91	9		....	... .	
14	....	....	86	14		....	....	
15	Y-O	....	80	20		....	....	
16	....	....	73.5	26.5		....	....	
17	O-Y	....	65	35		....	....	
18	....	....	56.5	43.5	....	....	....	
19	YO-Y	....	47	53		....	....	
20	....	....	36.5	63.5	....	....	....	
21	O-YY	....	25	75		....	....	
22	....	....	13.5	86.5		....	....	
23	Yellow	....	....	100		....	....	577
24	....	....	....	87	13	....	....	
25	YG-Y	....	....	75	25	....	....	
26	....	....	....	64	36	....	... .	
27	G-Y	....	....	55	45	....	....	
28	....	....	....	46	54	....	....	
29	GG-Y	....	....	39	61	....	....	
30	....	....	....	31	69	....	....	

1 As determined by Dr. P. G. Nutting, Associate Physicist, U. S. Bureau of Standards.

TABLE OF PERCENTAGES—Continued.

Number	Color.	Red.	Orange.	Yellow.	Green.	Blue.	Violet.	Wavelength.[1]
31	Y-G	......	....	24	76	....	....	
32	....	....	....	17	83	....	....	
33	GY-G	....	....	11	89	....	....	
34	....	....	....	6	94	....	....	
35	Green	....	....	....	100	....	....	520
36	....	....	....	....	96.5	3.5	....	
37	GB-G	....	....	....	93	7	....	
38	....	....	....	....	90	10	....	
39	B-G	....	....	....	85	15	....	
40	....	....	....	....	81	19	....	
41	BB-G	....	....	....	75	25	......	
42	....	....	....	....	69	31	....	
43	G-B	....	....	....	61	39	.. ....	
44	....	....	....	....	54	46	....	
45	BG-B	....	....	....	45	55	....	
46	....	....	....	....	36	64	....	
47	G-BB	....	....	....	25	75	....	
48	....	....	....	....	13	87	....	
49	Blue	....	....	....	....	100	....	473
50	....	....	....	....	....	84	16	
51	BV-B	....	....	....	....	72	28	
52	....	....	....	....	....	64	36	
53	V-B	....	....	....	....	54	46	
54	....	....	....	....	....	47	53	
55	B-V	....	....	....	....	40	60	
56	....	....	....	....	....	32	68	
57	VB-V	....	....	....	....	22	78	
58	....	....	....	....	....	12	88	
59	Violet	....	....	....	....	....	100	410
60	....	3	....	....	....	......	97	
61	VR-V	7	....	....	....	....	93	
62	....	11	....	....	....	....	89	
63	R-V	18	....	....	....	....	82	
64	....	24	....	....	....	....	76	
65	RR-V	33	....	....	....	....	67	
66	....	41	....	....	....	....	59	
67	V-R	52	....	....	....	....	48	
68	....	64	....	....	....	....	36	
69	RV-R	74	....	....	....	....	26	
70	....	83	....	....	....	....	17	
71	V-RR	90	....	....	....	....	10	
72	....	95.5	....	....	....	....	4.5	

[1] As determined by Dr. P. G. Nutting, Associate Physicist, U. S. Bureau of Standards.

TABLE SHOWING PERCENTAGE OF WHITE AND BLACK,
RESPECTIVELY, IN EACH TONE OF THE
TONE OR LUMINOSITY SCALES.

All of the vertical scales in the original Plates of this work (the scale of carbon grays alone excepted) contain the following percentages by color-wheel measurement :

TONE.	PERCENTAGES.		
	White.	Color.	Black.
(White)	100		
(g)	70	30	
f	45	55	
(e)	32	68	
d	22.5	77.5	
(c)	15	85	
b	9.5	90.5	
(a)	5	95	
(Full Color)		100	
(h)		64	26
i		55	45
(j)		41	59
k		29.5	70.5
(1)		20	80
m		12.5	87.5
(n)		6	94
(Black)			100

One of the most serious difficulties encountered in the preparation of the Plates of this work was the apparent impracticability of reproducing satisfactory shades of pure colors. This originated in the fact that there seems to be no substance (pigment, dye, or fabric) which represents a true black, all reflecting more or less of white light, and consequently producing shades which are dull or broken. The difficulty is increased by the additional fact that any black pigment mixed with almost any color falls short of even the color-wheel mixture in purity of hue in the resulting shades, owing to the very considerable amount of gray in all black pigments. Chromolithography can be made to produce clearer and better shades of the pure colors, but is distinctly objectionable for the purpose of a work of this kind owing to eventual oxidation of the oil or varnish with which the pigments are combined in lithographic inks, causing a change of hue; reds becoming more orange, blues more greenish, etc., in course of time.

While the absence (in large part) of pure chromatic shades is much to be regretted, the defect is not so serious, *from the standpoint of utility*, as might appear at first sight ; for while saturated or darkened pure colors are not uncommon in the animal, vegetable, and mineral kingdoms, more or less broken dark colors are infinitely more so; and since the latter are greatly increased in number by the defect mentioned the actual result is rather an advantage than otherwise.

It will doubtless be noticed that there is a conspicuous difference in relative darkness between shades of yellow and contiguous hues on the one hand and corresponding ones of violet and adjacent hues on the other, as if the percentage of black in each were very different. This, however, is entirely the result of difference of luminosity of the two sets of colors, that of yellow being between 70J0 and 8000 while that of violet is only about 1.3;* for the percentage of black in corresponding tones of the vertical scales is precisely the same for each color throughout the chromatic scale of this work.

---

*See Rood, Modern Chromatics, pages 34, 35.

TABLE SHOWING PERCENTAGES OF NEUTRAL GRAY
IN THE BROKEN COLOR SCALES.

Every Plate in each series of broken colors (′ to ′′′′′)
contains exactly the same percentage of neutral gray in
each color, the relative amount increasing progressively
in the several series, as shown in the followiug table.
The percentages of white in the tints and of black in the
shades of the tone scales are in all cases exactly the same
as in the tone scales of pure colors.

SERIES.	PERCENTAGES.	
	Color.	Neutral Gray.
Pure Colors	100	....
(′)	68	32
(″)	42	58
(‴)	23	77
(′′′′)	10	90
(′′′′′)	4.5	95.5
Neutral Gray	....	100

TABLE OF PERCENTAGE OF BLACK AND WHITE IN THE
DIFFERENT TONES OF CARBON GRAY.

TONE NUMBER.	PERCENTAGES.	
	Black.	White.
1	100	....
2	98	2
3	94.5	5.5
4	89.5	10.5
5	83	17
6	75	25
7	67.5	32.5
8	58.5	41.5
9	47	53
10	30	70

Note.—The percentages given in the preceding tables may not in all cases be precisely those actually contained in the colors on the Plates, since absolute preci-
sion in reproduction is hardly possible. All that can be claimed is a reasonably
close approximation to the ideal.

DYES AND PIGMENTS USED IN THE PREPARATION OF THE
MAXWELL DISKS, REPRESENTING THE THIRTY-
SIX COLORS OF THE PURE SPECTRUM SCALE,
FORMING THE BASIS OF THE COLOR-
SCHEME OF THIS WORK.*

Red.—Devoe's *geranium lake* (dry), its orange hue neutralized by a wash of *rhodamin b.* (*Crocein scarlet b.* washed with *rhodamin b.* produces practically the same fine red.)

Hues between red and orange.—*Crocein scarlet b.* with *gold orange.*

Orange.—*Gold orange* with *orange g.*

Hues between orange and yellow.—*Orange g.* with *auramin.*

Yellow.—*Auramin*, rather dilute. (The best substitute among pigments is a fine quality of *zinc yellow*, as Hatfield's.)

Hues between yellow and green.—*Auramin* washed with *light green.*

Green.—*Auramin* (very dilute) washed with *light green.* (The auramin should be applied first, because it "sets" or becomes fast quickly, while the light green does not, but is largely removed by overwashes of the yellow, thus rendering it very difficult to get the desired hue.)

Hues between green and blue.—*Methyl green;* the same washed with *light blue* (Diamond Dye); for the hues nearer blue, *light blue* washed with Winsor and Newton's *permanent blue* or *new blue* (the least violet-hued of the artificial ultramarines).

Blue.—*Light blue* washed with *permanent blue* or *new blue.* (Although the color is nearer that of the artificial ultramarines named, it is useless to apply the latter first,

---

*The aniline or coal-tar dyes named are all of the manufacture of Dr. G. Grübler and Co., Leipzig, Germany, unless otherwise stated. (See Preface, page ii.)

for overwashes of the light blue merely sink through and darken the color without improving the hue. A moderately saturated solution of the light blue should be applied first, and when this is dry covered with one or more rather thin washes of the permanent blue or new blue).

Hues between blue and violet.—Winsor and Newton's *permanent blue* and some of the more violet-hued artificial ultramarines, the hues nearer violet washed with *crystal violet* or *gentian violet*.　　·

Violet.—*Crystal violet.*

Hues between violet and red.—*Methyl violet 1b.* washed with *rhodamin b.;* for hues nearer red, *rhodamin b.* with Devoe's *geranium red* (dry) or *crocein scarlet b.*

While more or less similar in hue to rhodamin b., several other aniline dyes, as *acid fuchsin, rubin s., rosein, magenta,* etc., do not combine satisfactorily with the violets, the mixture soon becoming dark or dull and none of them are quite as pure a purple or red-violet.

It is most important to remember that disks thus colored must be carefully protected from light when not in actual use and *never* exposed to direct sunlight. The artificial ultramarines are, of course, permanent, and so, practically, are crocein scarlet, gold orange, orange g., and auramin—that is to say, are not materially affected by the action of light except after very prolonged exposure, though the last named undergoes a change of hue: but the green and violet aniline dyes are all very evanescent, rapidly fading and eventually disappearing; light blue and rhodamin, while sensitive to light, are far less so than the greens and violets.

ALPHABETICAL LIST OF COLORS REPRESENTED ON PLATES OF THIS WORK

COLOR NAME.	Plate.	Color or hue Number.	Tone.	COLOR NAME.	Plate	Color or hue Number.	Tone.
Absinthe Green	XXXI	29″	—	Benzo Brown	XLVI	13⁗	i
Acajou Red	XIII	1′	i	Benzol Green	VII	41	—
Acetin Blue	XXXV	49″	k	*Berlin Blue	VIII	47	m
Ackermann's Green	XVII	35′	k	Beryl Blue	VIII	43	f
Aconite Violet	XXXVII	63″	—	*Beryl Green	XIX	41′	b
Ageratum Violet	XXXVII	63″	b	*Bice Green	XVII	29′	k
Alice Blue	XXXIV	45″	b	Biscay Green	XXXI	27″	i
Alizarine Blue	XXI	51′	m	Bishop's Purple	XXXVII	65″	—
Alizarine Pink	XIII	1′	d	*Bister	XXIX	15″	m
Amaranth Pink	XII	69	d	Bittersweet Orange	II	9	b
Amaranth Purple	XII	69	i	Bittersweet Pink	II	9	d
Amber Brown	III	13	k	*Black	LIII	—	(1)
Amber Yellow	XVI	21′	b	Blackish Brown (1)	XLV	1⁗	m
American Green	XLI	33‴	i	Blackish Brown (2)	XLV	5⁗	m
Amethyst Violet	XI	61	—	Blackish Brown (3)	XLV	9⁗	m
Amparo Blue	IX	51	b	Blackish Green-Blue	VIII	43	m
Amparo Purple	XI	63	b	Blackish Green-Gray	LII	35⁗	m
Andover Green	XLVII	25⁗	i	Blackish Mouse Gray	LI	15⁗	m
Aniline Black	L	69⁗	m	Blackish Plumbeous	LII	49⁗	k
Aniline Lilac	XXXV	53″	d	Blackish Purple	XI	65	m
Aniline Yellow	IV	19	i	Blackish Red-Purple	XII	67	m
Anthracene Green	VII	39	m	*Blackish Slate	LIII	—	m(3)
Anthracene Purple	XLIV	69‴	k	Blackish Violet	X	59	m
Anthracene Violet	XXV	61′	k	Blackish Violet-Gray	LII	59⁗	m
Antimony Yellow	XV	17′	b	Blanc's Blue	XX	47′	k
Antique Brown	III	17	k	Blanc's Violet	XXIII	59′	k
Antique Green	VI	33	m	Blue-Violet	X	55	—
*Antwerp Blue	VIII	45	k	Blue-Violet Black	XLIX	57⁗	m
*Apple Green	XVII	29′	—	Bluish Black	XLIX	49⁗	m
Apricot Buff	XIV	11′	b	Bluish Glaucous	XLII	37‴	f
Apricot Orange	XIV	11′	—	Bluish Gray-Green	XLII	41‴	—
Apricot Yellow	IV	19	b	Bluish Lavender	XXXVI	57″	d
Argus Brown	III	13	m	Bluish Slate-Black	XLVIII	45⁗	m
Argyle Purple	XXXVII	65″	b	Bluish Violet	X	57	—
Army Brown	XL	13‴	i	Bone Brown	XL	13‴	m
Artemisia Green	XLVII	33⁗	—	Bordeaux	XII	71	k
Asphodel Green	XLI	29‴	—	*Bottle Green	XIX	37′	m
*Aster Purple	XII	67	i	Bradley's Blue	IX	51	—
Auburn	II	11	m	Bradley's Violet	XXIII	59′	—
*Auricula Purple	XXVI	69′	k	Brazil Red	I	5	i
Avellaneous	XL	17‴	b	Bremen Blue	XX	43′	b
Azurite Blue	IX	53	m	*Brick Red	XIII	5′	k
Barium Yellow	XVI	23′	d	Bright Chalcedony Yellow	XVII	25′	—
Baryta Yellow	IV	21	f	Bright Green-Yellow	V	9	—
*Bay	II	7	m	Brownish Drab	XLV	9⁗	—
Begonia Rose	I	1	b	Brownish Olive	XXX	19″	m

COLOR NAME.	Plate.	Color or hue Number.	Tone.	COLOR NAME.	Plate	Color or hue Number.	Tone.
Brownish Vinaceous	XXXIX	5'''	b	*China Blue	XX	45'	i
Brussels Brown	III	15	m	Chinese Violet	XXV	65'	b
Buckthorn Brown	XV	17'	i	*Chocolate	XXVIII	7''	m
*Buff-Pink	XXVIII	11''	d	*Chromium Green.	XXXII	31''	i
Buffy Brown	XL	17'''	l	Chrysolite Green	XXXI	27''	b
Buffy Citrine	XVI	19'	k	Chrysopraise Green	VII	37	b
Buffy Olive	XXX	21''	k	*Cinereous	LII	45'''''	d
*Buff-Yellow	IV	21	d	*Cinnamon	XXXI	15''	—
Burn Blue	XXXIV	47'	f	Cinnamon-Brown	XV	15''	k
Burnt Lake	XII	71	m	Cinnamon-Buff	XXIX	15''	d
*Burnt Sienna	II	9	k	Cinnamon-Drab	XLVI	13''''	—
*Burnt Umber	XXVIII	9''	m	*Cinnamon-Rufous	XIV	11'	i
Cacao Brown	XXVIII	9''	l	Citrine	IV	21	k
Cadet Blue	XXI	49'	i	Citrine-Drab	XL	19'''	i
Cadet Gray	XLII	45'''	b	Citron Green	XXXI	25''	b
*Cadmium Orange	III	13	—	*Citron Yellow	XVI	23'	b
*Cadmium Yellow	III	17	—	Civette Green	XVIII	31'	k
Calamine Blue	VIII	43	d	*Claret Brown	I	5	m
Calla Green	V	25	m	*Clay Color	XXIX	17''	—
Calliste Green	VI	31	i	Clear Cadet Blue	XXI	49'	—
Cameo Brown	XXVIII	7''	k	Clear Dull Green Yellow	XVII	25'	b
Cameo Pink	XXVI	71'	f	Clear Fluorite Green	XXXII	33''	b
*Campanula Blue	XXIV	57	b	Clear Blue-Green Gray	XLVIII	45'''''	d
Capri Blue	XX	43'	i	Clear Payne's Gray	XLIX	49'''''	b
Capucine Buff	III	13	f	Clear Windsor Blue	XXXV	49''	—
Capucine Orange	III	13	d	Clear Yellow-Green	VI	31	b
Capucine Yellow	III	15	b	*Clove Brown	XL	17'''	m
*Carmine	I	1	i	Cobalt Green	XIX	37'	b
Carnelian Red	XIV	7'	—	Colonial Buff	XXX	21''	d
Carob Brown	XIV	9'	m	Columbia Blue	XXXIV	47''	b
Carrot Red	XIV	7'	b	Commelina Blue	XXI	51'	—
Cartridge Buff	XXX	19''	f	Congo Pink	XXVIII	7''	b
Castor Gray	LII	35'''''	i	Coral Pink	XIII	5'	d
Cedar Green	VI	31	m	*Coral Red	XIII	5'	—
Celandine Green	XLVII	33'''''	b	Corinthian Pink	XXVII	3''	d
Cendre Blue	VIII	43	b	Corinthian Purple	XXXVIII	69''	k
Cendre Green	VI	35	b	Corinthian Red	XXVII	3''	—
Cerro Green	V	27	m	Cornflower Blue	XXI	53'	—
*Cerulean Blue	VIII	45	—	Corydalis Green	XLI	29'''	d
Chaetura Black	XLVI	17''''	m	Cossack Green	VI	33	m
Chaetura Drab	XLVI	17''''	k	Cosse Green	V	29	i
Chalcedony Yellow	XVII	25'	—	Cotinga Purple	XI	63	k
Chamois	XXX	19''	b	Courge Green	XVII	25'	i
Chapman's Blue	XXII	49*	i	Court Gray	XLVII	29'''''	f
Chartreuse Yellow	XXXI	25''	d	*Cream-Buff	XXX	19''	d
Chatenay Pink	XIII	3'	f	*Cream Color	XVI	19'	f
Chessylite Blue	XX	45'	k	Cress Green	XXXI	29''	k
*Chestnut	II	9	m	*Cyanine Blue	IX	51	m
Chestnut-Brown	XIV	11'	m	Dahlia Carmine	XXVI	71'	k
Chicory Blue	XXIV	59*	d	*Dahlia Purple	XII	67	k

COLOR NAME.	Plate.	Color or hue Number.	Tone.	COLOR NAME.	Plate	Color or hue Number.	Tone.
Danube Green	XXXII	35''	*m*	Dark Mouse Gray	LI	15'''''	*k*
Daphne Pink	XXXVIII	69''	*b*	Dark Naphthalene Violet	XXXVII	61''	*m*
Daphne Red	XXXVIII	69''	—	Dark Neutral Gray	LIII	—	*k*
Dark American Green	XLI	29'''	*k*	Dark Nigrosin Violet	XXV	65'	*m*
Dark Aniline Blue	X	55	*m*	Dark Olive	XL	21'''	*m*
Dark Anthracene Violet	XXV	61'	*m*	Dark Olive-Buff	XL	21'''	—
Dark Bluish Glaucous	XLII	37''''	*b*	Dark Olive-Gray	LI	23'''''	*i*
Dark Bluish Gray-Green	XLII	41''''	*k*	Dark Orient Blue	XXXIV	45''	*k*
Dark Bluish Violet	X	57	*m*	Dark Payne's Gray	XLIX	49'''''	*k*
Dark Cadet Blue	XXI	49'	*m*	Dark Perilla Purple	XXXVII	65''	*m*
Dark Chessylite Blue	XX	45'	*m*	Dark Plumbago Blue	XLIII	53'''	*b*
Dark Cinnabar Green	XIX	39'	*k*	Dark Plumbago Gray	L	61''''	—
Dark Citrine	IV	21	*m*	Dark Plumbago Slate	L	61''''	*k*
Dark Corinthian Purple	XXXIX	69''	*m*	Dark Plumbeous	LII	49'''''	*i*
Dark Cress Green	XXXI	29''	*m*	Dark Porcelain Green	XXXIII	39''	*k*
Dark Delft Blue	XLII	45'''	*m*	Dark Purple-Drab	XLV	1''''	*i*
Dark Diva Blue	XXI	51	*k*	Dark Purplish Gray	LIII	67'''''	*k*
Dark Dull Blue-Violet	XXXVI	55''	*k*	Dark Quaker Drab	LI	1'''''	*k*
Dark Dull Bluish Violet (1)	XXIV	57*	*k*	Dark Russian Green	XLII	37'''	*k*
Dark Dull Bluish Violet (2)	XXXV	51''	*k*	Dark Slate-Purple	XLIV	65'''	*k*
Dark Dull Bluish Violet (3)	XXXVI	57''	*k*	Dark Slate-Violet (1)	XLIII	57'''	*k*
Dark Dull Violet-Blue	XXIV	53*	*k*	Dark Slate-Violet (2)	XLIV	61'''	*k*
Dark Dull Yellow-Green	XXXII	31''	*m*	Dark Soft Blue-Violet	XXIII	55'	*k*
Dark Glaucous-Gray	XLVIII	37''''	*b*	Dark Soft Bluish Violet	XXIII	57'	*k*
Dark Gobelin Blue	XXXIV	43''	*k*	Dark Sulphate Green	XIX	39'	*i*
Dark Grayish Blue-Green	XLVIII	37'''''	*k*	Dark Terre Verte	XXXIII	41''	*k*
Dark Grayish Blue-Violet	XXIV	55*	*k*	Dark Tyrian Blue	XXXIV	47''	*k*
Dark Grayish Brown	XLV	5''''	*k*	Dark Varley's Gray	XLIX	57'''''	*k*
Dark Grayish Lavender	XLIII	57'''	*b*	Dark Vinaceous	XXVII	1''	—
Dark Grayish Olive	XLVI	21''''	*k*	Dark Vinaceous-Brown	XXXIX	5'''	*k*
Dark Green	XVIII	35'	*m*	Dark Vinaceous-Drab	XLV	5''''	*i*
Dark Green-Blue Gray	XLVIII	45''''	—	Dark Vinaceous-Gray	L	69''''	—
Dark Green-Blue Slate	XLVIII	45''''	*k*	Dark Vinaceous-Purple	XXXVIII	67''	*k*
Dark Greenish Glaucous	XLI	29''	*b*	Dark Violet	X	59	*k*
Dark Greenish Olive	XXX	23''	*m*	Dark Violet-Gray	LII	59'''''	*k*
Dark Gull Gray	LIII	—	(6)	Dark Violet-Slate	XLIX	53'''''	*k*
Dark Heliotrope Gray	L	65''''	—	Dark Viridian Green	VII	37	*k*
Dark Heliotrope Slate	L	65''''	*k*	Dark Yellowish Green	XVIII	33'	*m*
Dark Hyssop Violet	XXXVI	59''	*k*	Dark Yvette Violet	XXXVI	55''	*m*
Dark Indian Red	XXVII	3''	*m*	Dark Zinc Green	XIX	37'	*k*
Dark Ivy Green	XLVI	25''''	*k*	Dauphin's Violet	XXIII	59'	*i*
Dark Lavender	XLIV	61'''	*b*	Dawn Gray	LII	35'''''	*d*
Dark Livid Brown	XXXIX	1'''	*k*	Deep Aniline Lilac	XXXV	53''	*b*
Dark Livid Purple	XXXVII	63'''	*m*	Deep Blue-Violet	X	55	*i*
Dark Livid Red	XXXIX	1''	*k*	Deep Bluish Glaucous	XLII	37''''	*d*
Dark Madder Blue	XLIII	53'''	*k*	Deep Bluish Gray-Green	XLII	41''''	*i*
Dark Madder Violet	XXV	63'	*m*	Deep Brownish Drab	XLV	9''''	*i*
Dark Maroon Purple	XXVI	71'	*m*	Deep Brownish Vinaceous	XXXIX	5'''	—
Dark Medici Blue	XLVIII	41''''	*i*	Deep Cadet Blue	XXI	49'	*k*
Dark Mineral Red	XXVII	1''	*m*	Deep Chicory Blue	XXIV	57*	*b*

COLOR NAME.	Plate.	Color or hue Number.	Tone.	COLOR NAME.	Plate	Color or hue Number.	Tone.
*Deep Chrome	III	17	b	Deep Slate-Green	XLVII	33′′′′	k
Deep Chrysolite Green	XXXI	27′′	—	Deep Slate-Olive	XLVI	29′′′′	k
Deep Colonial Buff	XXX	21′′	b	Deep Slate-Violet	XLIV	61′′′	i
Deep Corinthian Red	XXVII	3′′	i	Deep Slaty Brown	L	69′′′′	k
Deep Delft Blue	XLII	45′′′	k	Deep Soft Blue-Violet	XXIII	55′	i
Deep Dull Bluish Violet (1)	XXIV	57*	i	Deep Soft Bluish Violet	XXIII	57′	i
Deep Dull Bluish Violet (2)	XXXV	51′′	i	Deep Turtle Green	XXXII	31′′	—
Deep Dull Bluish Violet (3)	XXXVI	57′′	i	Deep Varley's Gray	XLIX	57′′′′′	i
Deep Dull Lavender	XLIV	61′′′′′	d	Deep Vinaceous	XXVII	1′′	b
Deep Dull Violaceous Blue	XXII	51*	k	Deep Vinaceous-Gray	L	69′′′′	b
Deep Dull Violet-Blue	XXXV	53′′	i	Deep Vinaceous-Lavender	XLIV	65′′′	d
Deep Dull Yellow-Green (1)	XXXII	31′′	λ	Deep Violet-Gray	LII	59′′′′′	i
Deep Dull Yellow-Green (2)	XXXII	33′′	k	Deep Violet-Plumbeous	XLIX	53′′′′	—
Deep Dutch Blue	XLIII	49′′′	—	Deep Wedgewood Blue	XXI	51′	d
Deep Glaucous-Gray	XLVIII	37′′′	d	Delft Blue	XLII	45′′′	i
Deep Glaucous-Green	XXXII	39′′	b	Diamin-Azo Blue	XXXV	51′′	m
Deep Grape Green	XLI	25′′′	i	Diamine Brown	XIII	3′	m
Deep Grayish Blue-Green	XLVIII	37′′′′	i	Diamine Green	VII	37	m
Deep Grayish Lavender	XLIII	57′′	d	Diva Blue	XXI	51′	i
Deep Grayish Olive	XLVI	21′′′′	i	*Drab	XLVI	17′′′′	—
Deep Green-Blue Gray	XLVIII	45′′′′	b	*Drab-Gray	XLVI	17′′′′	d
Deep Greenish Glaucous	XLI	29′′′	d	*Dragons-blood Red	XIII	5′	i
Deep Gull Gray	LIII	—	b(?)	Dresden Brown	XV	17′	k
Deep Heliotrope Gray	L	65′′′′	b	Duck Green	XIX	39′	m
Deep Hellebore Red	XXXVIII	71′′	i	Dull Blackish Green	XLI	29′′	m
Deep Hyssop Violet	XXXVI	59′′	i	Dull Blue-Green Black	XLVIII	41′′′′	m
Deep Lavender	XXXVI	59′′	d	Dull Blue-Violet (1)	XXIV	55*	—
Deep Lavender-Blue	XXI	53′	b	Dull Blue-Violet (2)	XXXVI	55′′	i
Deep Lichen Green	XXXIII	37′′	d	Dull Bluish Violet (1)	XXIV	57*	—
Deep Livid Brown	XXXIX	1′′′	i	Dull Bluish Violet (2)	XXXV	51′′	i
Deep Livid Purple	XXXVII	63′′	k	Dull Bluish Violet (3)	XXXVI	57′′	—
Deep Madder Blue	XLIII	53′′′	ı	Dull Citrine	XVI	21′	k
Deep Malachite Green	XXXII	35′′	—	Dull Dark Purple	XXVI	67′	k
Deep Medici Blue	XLVIII	41′′′′	—	Dull Dusky Purple	XXVI	67′	m
Deep Mouse Gray	LI	15′′′′	i	Dull Greenish Black (1)	XLVII	29′′′′	m
Deep Neutral Gray	LIII	—	i	Dull Greenish Black (2)	XLVII	33′′′′	m
Deep Olive	XL	21′′′	k	Dull Green-Yellow	XVII	27′	—
Deep Olive-Buff	XL	21′′′	b	Dull Indian Purple	XLIV	69′′′	i
Deep Olive-Gray	LI	23′′′′′	—	Dull Lavender	XLIV	61′′′	f
Deep Orient Blue	XXXIV	45′′	i	Dull Magenta Purple	XXVI	67′	i
Deep Payne's Gray	XLIX	49′′′′	ı	Dull Opaline Green	XIX	37′	f
Deep Plumbago Blue	XLIII	53′′′	d	Dull Purplish Black	L	65′′′′	m
Deep Plumbago Gray	L	61′′′′	b	Dull Slate-Violet	XLIII	57′′′	i
Deep Plumbeous	LII	49′′′′′	—	Dull Violet-Black (1)	XLIV	61′′′	m
Deep Purplish Gray	LIII	67′′′′′	i	Dull Violet-Black (2)	XLIX	53′′′′	m
Deep Purplish Vinaceous	XLIV	69′′′	—	Dull Violet-Black (3)	L	61′′′′	m
Deep Quaker Drab	LI	1′′′′′	i	Dull Violaceous Blue	XXII	51*	—
Deep Rose-Pink	XII	71	d	Dull Violet-Blue	XXXV	53′′	—
Deep Seafoam Green	XXXI	27′′	d	Dusky Auricula Purple	XXVI	69′	m
Deep Slate-Blue	XLIII	49′′′	k	Dusky Blue	XXII	49*	m

COLOR NAME.	Plate.	Color or hue Number.	Tone.	COLOR NAME.	Plate	Color or hue Number.	Tone.
Dusky Blue-Green	XXXIII	39″	m	Fluorite Violet	XI	61	m
Dusky Bluish Green	XXXIII	41″	m	Forest Green	XVII	29′	m
Dusky Blue-Violet (1)	XXIII	57′	m	Forget-me-not Blue	XXII	51*	b
Dusky Blue-Violet (2)	XXIV	55*	m	*French Gray	LII	49‴″	f
Dusky Brown	XLV	1″″	k	*French Green	XXXII	35″	i
Dusky Drab	XLV	9″″	k	Fuscous	XLVI	13″″	k
Dusky Dull Bluish Green	XLII	41‴	m	Fuscous-Black	XLVI	13″″	m
Dusky Dull Green	XLII	37‴	m	Garnet Brown	I	3	k
Dusky Dull Violet (1)	XXXVI	57″	m	Gendarme Blue	XXII	47*	k
Dusky Dull Violet (2)	XXXVI	59″	m	Gentian Blue	XXI	53′	i
Dusky Dull Violet-Blue	XXXV	53″	m	*Geranium Pink	I	3	d
Dusky Green	XXXIII	37″	m	Glass Green	XXXI	29″	d
Dusky Green-Blue (1)	XX	43′	m	Glaucous	XLI	29‴	f
Dusky Green-Blue (2)	XXXIV	43″	m	*Glaucous-Blue	XXXIV	43″	b
Dusky Green-Gray	LII	35‴″	k	Glaucous-Gray	XLVIII	37″″	f
Dusky Greenish Blue	XX	47′	m	*Glaucous-Green	XXXIII	39″	d
Dusky Neutral Gray	LIII	—	m	Gnaphalium Green	XLVII	29″″	d
Dusky Olive-Green	XLI	25‴	m	Gobelin Blue	XXXIV	43″	i
Dusky Orient Blue	XXXIV	45″	m	Grape Green	XLI	25‴	—
Dusky Purplish Gray	LIII	67‴″	m	*Grass Green	VI	33	k
Dusky Slate-Blue	XLIII	49‴	m	Grayish Blue-Green	XLVIII	37″″	—
Dusky Slate-Violet	XLIII	57‴	m	Grayish Blue-Violet (1)	XXIV	55*	i
Dusky Violet	XXIII	59′	m	Grayish Blue-Violet (2)	XXXV	51″	b
Dusky Violet-Blue (1)	XXIII	55′	m	Grayish Lavender	XLIII	57‴	f
Dusky Violet-Blue (2)	XLIII	53″	m	Grayish Olive	XLVI	21″″	—
Dusky Yellowish Green	XLI	27‴	m	Grayish Violaceous Blue	XXII	51*	i
Dutch Blue	XLIII	49‴	b	Grayish Violet-Blue	XXIV	53*	i
*Ecru-Drab	XLVI	13″″	d	Green-Blue Slate	XLVIII	45″″	i
Ecru-Olive	XXX	21″	i	Green-Yellow	V	27	b
Elm Green	XVII	27′	m	Greenish Glaucous	XLI	33‴	f
*Emerald Green	VI	35	—	Greenish Glaucous-Blue	XLII	41‴	b
Empire Green	XXXII	33″	m	Greenish Slate-Black	XLVIII	37″″	m
Empire Yellow	IV	21	b	Greenish Yellow	V	25	—
Endive Blue	XLIII	49‴	d	Grenadine	II	7	b
English Red	II	7	i	Grenadine Pink	II	7	d
Eosine Pink	I	1	d	Grenadine Red	II	7	—
Etain Blue	XX	43′	f	Guinea Green	VII	39	i
Ethyl Green	VII	41	i	Gufl Gray	LIII	—	d(8)
Eton Blue	XXII	49*	k	Haematite Red	XXVII	5″	m
Etruscan Red	XXVII	5″	—	Haematoxylin Violet	XXV	61′	i
Eugenia Red	XIII	1′	—	*Hair Brown	XLVI	17″″	i
Eupatorium Purple	XXXVIII	67″	—	Hathi Gray	LII	35‴″	b
*Fawn Color	XL	13‴	—	Hay's Blue	IX	53	k
*Ferruginous	XIV	9′	i	Hay's Brown	XXXIX	9‴	k
*Flame Scarlet	II	9	—	Hay's Green	XVIII	33′	k
*Flax-flower Blue	XXI	51′	b	Hay's Lilac	XXXVII	63″	d
*Flesh Color	XIV	7′	d	Hay's Maroon	XIII	1′	m
Flesh Ocher	XIV	9′	b	Hay's Russet	XIV	7′	k
Flesh Pink	XIII	5′	f	*Hazel	XIV	11′	k
Fluorite Green	XXXII	33″	—	Heliotrope-Gray	L	65″″	d

COLOR NAME.	Plate	Color or hue Number.	Tone.	COLOR NAME.	Plate	Color or hue Number.	Tone.
Heliotrope-Slate	L	65''''	i	Light Alice Blue	XXXIV	45''	d
Hellebore Green	XVII	25'	m	Light Amparo Blue	IX	51	d
Hellebore Red	XXXVIII	71''	—	Light Amparo Purple	XI	63	d
Helvetia Blue	IX	51	k	Light Bice Green	XVII	29'	i
Hermosa Pink	I	1	f	Light Blue-Green	VII	39	d
Hessian Brown	XIII	5'	m	Light Blue-Violet	X	55	b
Honey Yellow	XXX	19''	—	Light Bluish Violet	X	57	b
Hortense Blue	XXII	47*	m	Light Brownish Drab	XLV	9''''	b
Hortense Violet	XI	61	b	Light Brownish Olive	XXX	19'''	k
*Hyacinth Blue	X	55	k	Light Brownish Vinaceous	XXXIX	5'''	d
Hyacinth Violet	XI	61	i	Light Buff	XV	17'	f
Hydrangea Pink	XXVII	5''	f	Light Cadet Blue	XXI	49'	b
Hydrangea Red	XXVII	1''	i	Light Cadmium	IV	19	—
Hyssop Violet	XXXVI	59''	—	Light Campanula Blue	XXIV	55*	d
Indian Lake	XXVI	71'	i	Light Celandine Green	XLVII	33''''	d
*Indian Purple	XXXVIII	67''	m	Light Cendre Green	VI	35	d
Indian Red	XXVII	3''	k	Light Cerulean Blue	VIII	45	b
*Indigo Blue	XXXIV	47''	m	Light Chalcedony Yellow	XVII	25'	d
Indulin Blue	XXII	51*	m	Light Chicory Blue	XXIV	57*	f
Invisible Green	XIX	41'	m	Light Cinnamon-Drab	XLVI	13''''	b
Iron Gray	LI	23'''''	k	Light Columbia Blue	XXXIV	47''	d
*Isabella Color	XXX	19''	i	Light Congo Pink	XXVIII	7''	d
Italian Blue	VIII	43	—	Light Coral Red	XIII	5'	b
Ivory Yellow	XXX	21''	f	Light Corinthian Red	XXVII	3''	b
Ivy Green	XXXI	25''	m	Light Cress Green	XXXI	29''	i
Jade Green	XXXI	27''	k	Light Danube Green	XXXII	35''	k
Japan Rose	XXVIII	9'''	b	Light Drab	XLVI	17''''	b
Jasper Green	XXXIII	37''	i	Light Dull Bluish Violet	XXXVI	57''	b
Jasper Pink	XIII	3'	d	Light Dull Green-Yellow	XVII	27'	b
Jasper Red	XIII	3'	—	Light Elm Green	XVII	27'	i
Javel Green	V	27	i	Light Fluorite Green	XXXII	33''	d
Jay Blue	XXII	47*	i	Light Forget-me-not Blue	XXII	51*	d
Jovence Blue	XX	43'	k	Light Glaucous-Blue	XXXIV	43'	d
Kaiser Brown	XIV	9'	k	Light Dull Glaucous-Blue	XLII	41''''	d
Kildare Green	XXXI	29''	b	Light Grape Green	XLI	25'''	b
Killarney Green	XVIII	35'	i	Light Grayish Blue-Violet	XXXV	51''	b
King's Green	XXII	47*	b	Light Grayish Olive	XLVI	21''''	b
Kronberg's Green	XXXI	25''	k	Light Grayish Vinaceous	XXXIX	9'''	d
Laelia Pink	XXXVIII	67''	d	Light Grayish Violet-Blue	XXIV	53*	d
La France Pink	I	3	f	Light Greenish Yellow	V	25	b
*Lavender	XXXVI	59''	f	Light Green-Yellow	V	27	d
Lavender-Blue	XXI	53'	d	Light Gull Gray	LIII		f (9)
*Lavender-Gray	XLIII	49''	f	Light Heliotrope-Gray	L	65''''	f
Lavender-Violet	XXV	61'	b	Light Hellebore Green	XVII	25'	k
Leaf Green	XLI	29'''	k	Light Hortense Violet	XI	61	d
Leitch's Blue	VIII	47	i	Light Hyssop Violet	XXXVI	59''	b
Lemon Chrome	IV	21	—	Light Jasper Red	XIII	3'	b
*Lemon Yellow	IV	23	—	Light King's Blue	XXII	47*	d
Lettuce Green	V	29	k	Light Lavender-Blue	XXI	53'	f
Lichen Green	XXXIII	37''	f	Light Lavender-Violet	XXV	61'	d

COLOR NAME.	Plate.	Color or hue Number.	Tone.	COLOR NAME.	Plate	Color or hue Number.	Tone.
Light Lobelia Violet	XXXVII	61″	d	Light Viridine Green	VI	33	f
Light Lumiere Green	XVII	29′	d	Light Viridine Yellow	V	29	d
Light Mallow Purple	XII	67	d	Light Windsor Blue	XXXV	49″	b
Light Mauve	XXV	63′	d	Light Wistaria Blue	XXIII	57′	d
Light Medici Blue	XLVIII	41″″	d	Light Wistaria Violet	XXIII	59′	d
Light Methyl Blue	VIII	47	b	Light Yellow-Green	VI	31	d
Light Mineral Gray	XLVII	25″″	f	Light Yellowish Olive	XXX	23″	i
Light Mouse Gray	LI	15″″″	b	*Lilac	XXV	65′	d
Light Neropalin Blue	XXII	49*		*Lilac-Gray	LII	59″″″	f
Light Neutral Gray	LIII	—	b	Lily Green	XLVII	33″″	i
Light Niagara Green	XXXIII	41″	d	Lime Green	XXXI	25″	—
Light Ochraceous-Buff	XV	15′	d	Lincoln Green	XLI	25″″	k
Light Ochraceous-Salmon	XV	13′	d	Liseran Purple	XXVI	67′	b
Light Olive-Gray	LI	23″″″	d	Litho Purple	XXV	63′	i
Light Orange-Yellow	III	17	d	*Liver Brown	XIV	7′	m
Light Oriental Green	XVIII	33′	b	Livid Brown	XXXIX	1″″	—
Light Paris Green	XVIII	35′	d	Livid Pink	XXVII	3″	f
Light Payne's Gray	XLIX	49″″	d	Livid Purple	XXXVII	63″	i
Light Perilla Purple	XXXVII	65″	i	Livid Violet	XXXVII	61″	i
Light Phlox Purple	XI	65	d	Lobelia Violet	XXXVII	61″	b
Light Pinkish Cinnamon	XXIX	15″	d	Lumiere Blue	XX	43′	d
Light Pinkish Lilac	XXXVII	65″	f	Lumiere Green	XVII	29′	b
Light Plumbago Gray	L	61″″	f	Lyons Blue	IX	51	i
Light Porcelain Green	XXXIII	39″	—	Madder Blue	XLIII	53″′	—
Light Purple-Drab	XLV	1″″	b	*Madder Brown	XIII	3′	k
Light Purplish Gray	LIII	67″″″	b	Madder Violet	XXV	63′	k
Light Purplish Vinaceous	XXXIX	1″′	d	*Magenta	XXVI	67′	—
Light Quaker Drab	LI	1″″″	b	Mahogany Red	II	7	k
Light Rosolane Purple	XXVI	69′	b	*Maize Yellow	III	19	f
Light Russet-Vinaceous	XXXIX	9″′	b	*Malachite Green	XXXII	35″	b
Light Salmon-Orange	II	11	d	Mallow Pink	XII	67	f
Light Seal Brown	XXXIX	9″′	m	Mallow Purple	XII	67	b
Light Sky Blue	XX	47′	f	Manganese Violet	XXV	63′	—
Light Soft Blue-Violet	XXIII	55′	b	Marguerite Yellow	XXX	23″	J
Light Squill Blue	XX	45′	d	*Marine Blue	VIII	45	m
Light Sulphate Green	XIX	39′	b	*Maroon	I	3	m
Light Terre Verte	XXXIII	41″	—	*Mars Brown	XV	13′	m
Light Turtle Green	XXXII	31″	d	Mars Orange	II	9	
Light Tyrian Blue	XXXIV	47″	—	Mars Violet	XXXVIII	71″	m
Light Varley's Gray	XLIX	57″″	b	Mars Yellow	III	15	i
Light Vinaceous-Cinnamon	XXIX	13″	d	Martius Yellow	III	23	f
Light Vinaceous-Drab	XLV	5″″	b	Massicot Yellow	XVI	21′	J
Light Vinaceous-Fawn	XL	13″′	d	Mathews' Blue	XX	45′	—
Light Vinaceous-Gray	L	69″″	f	Mathews' Purple	XXV	65′	—
Light Vinaceous-Lilac	XLIV	69″′	d	*Mauve	XXV	63′	b
Light Vinaceous-Purple	XLIV	65″′	b	Mauvette	XXV	65′	f
Light Violet	X	59	b	Mazarine Blue	IX	49	d
Light Violet-Blue	IX	53	b	Meadow Green	VI	35	k
Light Violet-Gray	LII	59″″″	b	Medal Bronze	III	19	m
Light Violet-Plumbeous	XLIX	53″″	d	Medici Blue	XLVIII	41″″	b

COLOR NAME.	Plate.	Color or hue Number.	Tone.	COLOR NAME.	Plate	Color or hue Number.	Tone.
Methyl Blue	VIII	47	—	*Olive-Buff	XL	21'''	d
Methyl Green	XIX	41'	—	Olive-Citrine	XVI	21'	m
Microcline Green	XIX	39'	f	*Olive-Gray	LI	23'''''	b
Mignonette Green	XXXI	25''	i	*Olive-Green	IV	23	m
Mikado Brown	XXIX	13''	i	Olive Lake	XVI	21'	i
Mikado Orange	III	13	b	Olive-Ocher	XXX	21''	—
Mineral Gray	XLVII	25''''	d	*Olive-Yellow	XXX	23''	—
Mineral Green	XVIII	31'	—	Olivine	XXXII	35''	d
Mineral Red	XXVII	1''	k	Olympic Blue	XX	47'	—
Montpellier Green	XXXIII	37''	—	Onion-skin Pink	XXVIII	11''	b
Morocco Red	I	5	k	Ontario Violet	XXXVI	55''	b
Motmot Blue	XX	43'	—	Opaline Green	VII	37	f
Motmot Green	XVIII	35'	—	*Orange	II	15	—
*Mouse Gray	LI	15'''''	—	*Orange-Buff	III	15	d
*Mummy Brown	XV	17'	m	*Orange Chrome	II	11	—
Mulberry Purple	XI	61	k	Orange-Cinnamon	XXIX	13''	—
Mustard Yellow	XVI	19'	b	Orange-Citrine	IV	19	k
Mytho Green	XLI	29'''	b	Orange-Pink	II	11	f
*Myrtle Green	VII	41	m	*Orange-Rufous	II	11	i
Naphthalene Violet	XXXVII	61'	k	Orange-Vinaceous	XXVII	5''	d
Naphthalene Yellow	XVI	23'	f	Oriental Green	XVIII	33'	—
*Naples Yellow	XVI	19'	d	Orient Blue	XXXIV	45''	—
Natal Brown	XL	13'''	k	Orient Pink	II	9	f
Navy Blue	XXI	53'	m	Oural Green	XVIII	35'	f
Neropalin Blue	XXII	49*	b	Ox-blood Red	I	1	k
Neutral Gray	LIII	—	—	Oxide Blue	VIII	45	i
Neutral Red	XXXVIII	71''	k	Pale Amaranth Pink	XII	63	f
Neuvider Green	VII	37	d	Pale Amparo Blue	IX	51	f
Neva Green	V	29	—	Pale Amparo Purple	XI	63	f
Niagara Green	XXXIII	41''	b	Pale Aniline Lilac	XXXV	53''	f
Nickel Green	XXXIII	37''	k	*Pale Blue (Ethyl Blue)	VIII	45	f
Night Green	VI	33	—	Pale Blue-Green	VII	39	f
Nigrosin Blue	XXXV	49''	m	Pale Blue-Violet	X	55	d
Nigrosin Violet	XXV	65'	k	Pale Bluish Lavender	XXXVI	57''	f
*Nile Blue	XIX	41'	d	Pale Bluish Violet	X	57	d
Nopal Red	I	3	i	Pale Brownish Drab	XLV	5''''	d
*Ochraceous-Buff	XV	15'	b	Pale Brownish Vinaceous	XXXIX	3'''	f
Ochraceous-Orange	XV	15'	—	Pale Cadet Blue	XXI	49'	d
Ochraceous-Salmon	XV	13'	b	Pale Campanula Blue	XXIV	57*	d
Ochraceous-Tawny	XV	15'	i	Pale Cendre Green	VI	35	f
Ocher Red	XXVII	5''	b	Pale Cerulean Blue	VIII	45	d
*Oil Green	V	27	k	Pale Chalcedony Yellow	XVII	25'	f
Oil Yellow	V	25	i	Pale Cinnamon-Pink	XXIX	13''	f
Old Gold	XVI	19'	i	Pale Congo Pink	XXVIII	7''	f
Old Rose	XIII	1'	b	Pale Drab-Gray	XLVI	17''''	d
Olivaceous Black (1)	XLVI	21''''	m	Pale Dull Glaucous-Blue	XLII	43''	f
Olivaceous Black (2)	XLVII	25''''	m	Pale Dull Green-Yellow	XVII	27'	f
Olivaceous Black (3)	LI	23'''''	m	Pale Ecru-Drab	XLVI	13''''	f
*Olive	XXX	21''	m	Pale Flesh Color	XIV	7'	f
Olive-Brown	XL	17'''	m	Pale Fluorite Green	XXXII	33''	f

COLOR NAME.	Plate.	Color or hue Number.	Tone.	COLOR NAME.	Plate	Color or hue Number.	Tone.
Pale Forget-me-not Blue...	XXII	51*	f	Pale Sulphate Green.......	XIX	39'	d
Pale Glass Green..........	XXXI	29''	f	Pale Tiber Green..........	XVIII	33'	f
Pale Glaucous-Blue........	XXXIV	43''	f	Pale Turquoise Green......	VII	41	f
Pale Glaucous-Green.......	XXXIII	39''	f	Pale Turtle Green..........	XXXII	31''	f
Pale Grayish Blue.........	XXI	49'	f	Pale Varley's Gray.........	XLIX	57'''''	d
Pale Grayish Blue-Violet...	XXXV	51''	f	Pale Verbena Violet.	XXXVI	55''	f
Pale Grayish Vinaceous....	XXXIX	5'''	f	Pale Veronese Green......	XVIII	31'	f
Pale Grayish Violet-Blue...	XXIV	53*	d	Pale Vinaceous.........	XXVII	1''	f
Pale Greenish Yellow......	V	25	d	Pale Vinaceous-Drab.......	XLV	3''''	d
Pale Green-Blue Gray.....	XLVIII	43''''	f	Pale Vinaceous-Fawn......	XL	13'''	f
Pale Green-Yellow........	V	27	f	Pale Vinaceous-Lilac.	XLIV	69'''	—
Pale Gull Gray............	LIII	—	(10)	Pale Vinaceous-Pink.......	XXVIII	9''	f
Pale Hortense Violet	XI	61	f	Pale Violet..............	X	59	d
Pale King's Blue	XXII	47*	f	Pale Violet-Blue..........	IX	53	d
Pale Laelia Pink...........XXXVIII		67''	f	Pale Violet-Gray...........	LII	59'''''	d
Pale Lavender-Violet......	XXV	61'	f	Pale Violet-Plumbeous.....	XLIX	53''''	f
Pale Lemon Yellow	IV	23	b	Pale Viridine Yellow.......	V	29	f
Pale Lilac..................	XXXVII	63''	f	Pale Windsor Blue.........	XXXV	49''	d
Pale Lobelia Violet........	XXXVII	61''	f	Pale Wistaria Blue.........	XXIII	57''	f
Pale Lumiere Green......	XVII	29'	f	Pale Wistaria Violet.......	XXIII	59'	f
Pale Mauve....	XXV	63'	f	Pale Yellow-Green..........	VI	31	f
Pale Mazarine Blue.......	IX	49	f	Pale Yellow-Orange........	III	15	f
Pale Medici Blue..........	XLVIII	41''''	f	Pallid Blue-Violet..........	X	55	f
Pale Methyl Blue..........	VIII	47	d	Pallid Bluish Violet.......	X	57	f
Pale Mouse Gray..........	LI	15'''''	d	Pallid Brownish Drab.....	XLV	5''''	f
Pale Neropalin Blue.....	XXII	49*	f	Pallid Grayish Violet-Blue..	XXIV	53*	f
Pale Neutral Gray.........	LIII	—	d	Pallid Methyl Blue.........	VIII	47	f
Pale Niagara Green........	XXXIII	41''	f	Pallid Mouse Gray........	LI	15'''''	f
Pale Nile Blue.............	XIX	41'	f	Pallid Neutral Gray.......	LIII	—	f
Pale Ochraceous-Buff......	XV	15'	f	Pallid Purple-Drab.........	XLV	1''''	f
Pale Ochraceous-Salmon	XV	13'	f	Pallid Purplish Gray.......	LIII	67'''''	f
Pale Olive-Buff	XL	21'''	f	Pallid Quaker Drab........	LI	1'''''	f
Pale Olive-Gray	LI	23'''''	d	Pallid Soft Blue-Violet.....	XXIII	55'	f
Pale Olivine...............	XXXII	35''	f	Pallid Vinaceous-Drab......	XLV	3''''	f
Pale Orange-Yellow........	III	17	f	Pallid Violet..............	X	59	f
Pale Payne's Gray.........	XLIX	49''''	f	Pallid Violet-Blue..........	IX	53	f
Pale Persian Lilac....,.....XXXVIII		69''	f	*Pansy Purple.............	XII	69	k
Pale Pinkish Buff..........	XXIX	17''	f	Pansy Violet	XI	63	i
Pale Pinkish Cinnamon....	XXIX	15''	f	*Paris Blue...............	VIII	47	k
Pale Purple-Drab.....	XLV	1''''	d	*Paris Green..............	XVIII	35'	b
Pale Purplish Gray........	LIII	67'''''	d	*Parrot Green.............	VI	31	k
Pale Purplish Vinaceous...	XXXIX	1'''	f	Parula Blue...............	XLII	43'''	—
Pale Quaker Drab..........	LI	1'''''	d	Patent Blue...............	VIII	43	k
Pale Rhodonite Pink.......XXXVIII		71''	f	Payne's Gray..............	XLIX	49	
Pale Rose-Purple	XXVI	67'	f	Peach Red................	I	5	b
Pale Rosolane Purple......	XXVI	69'	d	Peacock Blue..............	VIII	43	i
Pale Russian Blue.........	XLII	43'''	f	Peacock Green	VI	35	i
Pale Salmon Color........	XIV	9'	f	*Pea Green................	XLVII	29'''''	b
Pale Smoke Gray..........	XLVI	21''''	f	*Pearl Blue................	XXXV	49''	f
Pale Soft Blue-Violet.	XXIII	55'	d	*Pearl Gray......	LII	35'''''	f

COLOR NAME.	Plate,	Color or hue Number.	Tone.	COLOR NAME.	Plate	Color or hue Number.	Tone.
Pecan Brown	XXVIII	11″	i	Rhodonite Pink	XXXVIII	71″	d
Perilla Purple	XXXVII	65″	k	Rinnemann's Green	XVIII	31′	i
Persian Blue	XX	45′	f	Rivage Green	XVIII	31′	b
Persian Lilac	XXXVIII	69″	d	Rocellin Purple	XXXVIII	71″	b
Petunia Violet	XXV	65′	i	Roman Green	XVI	23′	m
Phenyl Blue	IX	53	—	Rood's Blue	IX	49	k
Phlox Pink	XI	65	f	Rood's Brown	XXVIII	11″	k
*Phlox Purple	XI	65	b	Rood's Lavender	XLIX	57″″″	f
Picric Yellow	IV	23	d	Rood's Violet	XI	65	i
Pinard Yellow	IV	21	d	Rose Color	XII	71	b
*Pinkish Buff	XXIX	17″	d	Rose Doree	I	3	b
Pinkish Cinnamon	XXIX	15″	b	*Rose Pink	XII	71	f
*Pinkish Vinaceous	XXVII	5″	d	*Rose-Purple	XXVI	67′	d
Pistachio Green	XLI	33‴	—	*Rose Red	XII	71	—
Pleroma Violet	XXV	61′	—	Rosolane Pink	XXVI	69′	f
Plumbago Blue	XLIII	53″″	f	Rosolane Purple	XXVI	69′	—
Plumbago Gray	L	61″″″	d	Roslyn Blue	X	57	k
Plumbago Slate	L	61″″″	i	*Royal Purple	X	59	k
*Plumbeous	LII	49″″″″	b	*Rufous	XIV	9′	—
Plumbeous-Black	LII	49″″″″	m	*Russet	XV	13′	k
*Plum Purple	XXIV	57*	m	Russet-Vinaceous	XXXIX	9‴	—
Pois Green	XLI	29‴	i	Russian Blue	XLII	45‴	d
*Pomegranate Purple	XII	71	i	Russian Green	XLII	37″″	i
Porcelain Blue	XXXIV	43″	—	Saccardo's Olive	XVI	19′	m
Porcelain Green	XXXIII	39″	i	Saccardo's Slate	XLVIII	41″″″	k
Pompeian Red	XIII	3′	i	Saccardo's Umber	XXIX	17″	k
*Primrose Yellow	XXX	23″	d	Saccardo's Violet	XXXVII	61″	k
Primuline Yellow	XVI	19′	—	Safrano Pink	II	7	f
*Prout's Brown	XV	15′	m	*Sage Green	XLVII	29″″″	k
*Prune Purple	XI	63	m	Sailor Blue	XXI	53′	k
Prussian Blue	IX	49	m	*Salmon-Buff	XIV	11′	d
Prussian Green	XIX	41′	k	*Salmon Color	XIV	9′	d
Prussian Red	XXVII	5″	k	Salmon-Orange	II	11	b
Puritan Gray	XLVII	33″″	f	Salvia Blue	IX	49	b
Purple (true)	XI	65	—	Sanford's Brown	II	11	k
Purple-Drab	XLV	1″″	—	Sayal Brown	XXIX	15″	—
Purplish Gray	LIII	67″″	—	*Scarlet	I	5	—
Purplish Lilac	XXXVII	65″	d	Scarlet-Red	I	3	—
Purplish Vinaceous	XXXIX	1‴	b	Scheele's Green	VI	33	i
Pyrite Yellow	IV	23	i	Schoenfeld's Purple	XXVI	69′	i
Quaker Drab	LI	1″″	—	Seafoam Green	XXXI	27″	f
Rainette Green	XXXI	27″	i	Seafoam Yellow	XXXI	25″	f
Ramier Blue	XLIII	57‴	—	*Sea Green	XIX	41′	i
Raisin Black	XLIV	65‴	m	*Seal Brown	XXXIX	5″″	m
Raisin Purple	XI	65	k	Seashell Pink	XIV	11′	f
*Raw Sienna	III	17	i	*Sepia	XXIX	17″	m
*Raw Umber	III	17	m	Serpentine Green	XVI	23′	k
Reed Yellow	XXX	23″	b	Shamrock Green	XXXII	33″	i
Rejane Green	XXXIII	37″	b	Shell Pink	XXVIII	11″	f
Rhodamine Purple	XII	67	—	Shrimp Pink	I	5	f

COLOR NAME.	Plate.	Color or hue Number.	Tone.	COLOR NAME.	Plate	Color or hue Number.	Tone.
Skobeloff Green	VII	39	—	Tyrian Rose	XII	69	—
Sky Blue	XX	47'	d	Tyrolite Green	VII	39	b
Sky Gray	XXXIV	45''	f	Ultramarine Ash	XXII	49*	—
*Slate-Black	LIII	—	(2)	*Ultramarine Blue	IX	49	i
Slate-Blue	XLIII	49''	i	Urania Blue	XXIV	53*	m
*Slate Color	LIII	—	k(4)	Vanderpoel's Blue	XX	47'	i
*Slate-Gray	LIII	—	i(5)	Vanderpoel's Green	VI	33	b
Slate-Olive	XLVII	29''''	i	Vanderpoel's Violet	XXXVI	55''	—
Slate-Purple	XLIV	65'''	i	*Vandyke Brown	XXVIII	11''	m
Slate-Violet (1)	XLIII	57'''	i	Vandyke Red	XIII	1'	k
Slate-Violet (2)	XLIV	61'''	—	Variscite Green	XIX	37'	d
*Smalt Blue	IX	53	i	Varley's Gray	XLIX	57''''	—
*Smoke Gray	XLVI	21''''	d	Varley's Green	XVIII	31'	m
Snuff Brown	XXIX	15''	k	Venetian Blue	XXII	47*	—
Soft Blue-Violet	XXIII	55'	k	Venetian Pink	XIII	1'	f
Soft Bluish Violet	XXIII	57'	—	Venice Green	VII	41	b
Sooty Black	LI	1''''	m	Verbena Violet	XXXVI	55''	d
Sorghum Brown	XXXIX	9'''	i	*Verdigris Green	XIX	37'	—
Sorrento Green	VII	41	k	Vernonia Purple	XXVIII	69''	i
Spectrum Blue	IX	49	—	Verona Brown	XXIX	13''	k
Spectrum Red	I	1	—	Veronese Green	XVIII	31'	d
Spectrum Violet	X	59	—	Vetiver Green	XLVII	25''''	—
Spinach Green	V	29	m	Victoria Lake	I	1	m
Spinel Pink	XXVI	71'	b	*Vinaceous	XXVII	1''	d
Spinel Red	XXVI	71'	—	Vinaceous-Brown	XXXIX	5'''	i
Squill Blue	XX	45'	b	*Vinaceous-Buff	XL	17''''	d
Stone Green	XLII	37'''	—	*Vinaceous-Cinnamon	XXIX	13''	b
Storm Gray	LII	35'''''	—	Vinaceous-Drab	XLV	5'''	—
Strawberry Pink	I	5	d	Vinaceous-Fawn	XL	13''''	b
*Straw Yellow	XVI	21'	d	Vinaceous-Gray	L	69''''	d
Strontian Yellow	XVI	23'	—	Vinaceous-Lavender	XLIV	65'''	f
Sudan Brown	III	15	k	Vinaceous-Lilac	XLIV	69'''	b
Sulphate Green	XIX	39'	—	*Vinaceous-Pink	XXVII	9''	d
Sulphin Yellow	IV	21	i	Vinaceous-Purple (1)	XXXVIII	67''	i
*Sulphur Yellow	V	25	f	Vinaceous-Purple (2)	XLIV	65'''	—
Taupe Brown	XLIV	69'''	m	*Vinaceous-Rufous	XIV	7'	i
*Tawny	XV	13'	i	Vinaceous-Russet	XXVIII	7''	—
*Tawny-Olive	XXXIX	17''	i	Vinaceous-Slate	L	69''''	i
Tea Green	XLVII	25''''	b	Vinaceous-Tawny	XXVIII	11''	—
Terra Cotta	XXVIII	7''	—	Violet Carmine	XII	69	m
*Terre Verte	XXXIII	41''	i	Violet-Gray	LII	59'''''	—
Testaceous	XXVIII	9''	—	Violet-Plumbeous	XLIX	53''''	b
Thulite Pink	XXVI	71'	d	Violet-Purple	XI	63	—
Tiber Green	XVIII	33'	d	Violet-Slate	XLIX	53''''	i
Tilleul Buff	XL	17'''	f	Violet Ultramarine	X	57	i
Tourmaline Pink	XXXVIII	67''	b	*Viridian Green	VII	37	i
Turquoise Green	VII	41	d	Viridine Green	VI	33	d
Turtle Green	XXXII	31''	b	Viridine Yellow	V	29	b
Tyrian Blue	XXXIV	47''	i	Vivid Green	VII	37	—
Tyrian Pink	XII	69	b	Wall Green	VII	39	k

COLOR NANE.	Plate.	Color or hue Number.	Tone.	COLOR NAME.	Plate.	Color or hue Number.	Tone.
*Walnut Brown	XXVIII	9″	k	*Wood Brown	XL	17‴′	—
Warbler Green	IV	23	k	Xanthine Orange	III	13	ι
Warm Blackish Brown	XXXIX	1‴	m	Yale Blue	XX	47′	b
Warm Buff	XV	17′	d	Yellow-Green	VI	31	—
Warm Sepia	XXIX	13″	m	Yellowish Citrine	XVI	23′	ι
Water Green	XLI	25‴	d	Yellowish Glaucous	XLI	25‴	f
*Wax Yellow	XVI	21′	—	Yellowish Oil Green	V	25	k
Wedgewood Blue	XXI	51′	f	Yellowish Olive	XXX	23″	k
White	LIII‡	—	—	Yellow Ocher	XV	17′	—
Windsor Blue	XXXV	49″	i	Yew Green	XXXI	27″	m
Winter Green	XVIII	33′	i	Yvette Violet	XXXVI	55″	k
Wistaria Blue	XXIII	57′	b	Zinc Green	XIX	37′	i
Wistaria Violet	XXIII	59′	b	Zinc Orange	XV	13′	—

‡Also the top horizontal row on all the other plates.

THE FOLLOWING COLORS REPRESENTED IN THE OLD "NOMEN-
CLATURE OF COLORS" (1886) CANNOT BE MATCHED BY COLORS IN
THE PRESENT WORK. THEY ARE INTERMEDIATES, EITHER AS TO
HUE OR TONE (SOMETIMES BOTH), AND WOULD FALL IN UNCOLORED
SPACES, AS INDICATED BY THE NUMERALS AND LETTERS APPENDED
TO EACH:—

Azure Blue=48 *a* (see Plates VIII and IX).
Broccoli Brown: Between 17''' *k* and 17'''' *i* (see Plates XL and XLVI).
Buff=18'' *d* (see Plates III and IV).
Burnt Carmine=71 *i* (Plate XII).
Canary Yellow: Between 23 *b* and 21' *b* (see Plates IV and XVI).
Chinese Orange=12 *h* (see Plates II and III).
Chrome Yellow=20 *a* (Plate IV).
Cobalt Blue=48 slightly dull (see Plates VIII and IX).
Crimson=1 *j* (Plate I).
French Blue=52 *h* (Plate IX).
Gallstone Yellow=19' *h* (Plate XVI).
Gamboge Yellow=20, slightly dull, or 21, slightly dull (Plate IV).
Geranium Red=3 *a* (Plate I).
Heliotrope Purple: Between 65''' *b* and 65'''' *b* (see Plates XLIV and L).
Indian Yellow=18 *h* or 18 slightly dull (Plate III). This color and Saffron Yellow
    are practically identical in many copies of the old "Nomenclature."
Lake Red=72 *h* (Plate XII).
Maroon Purple=72' *i* (Plate XXVI).
Ochraceous=16' *h* (Plate XV).
Ochraceous-Rufous=12' *h* (see Plates XIV and XV).
Ochre Yellow=18' (see Plates XV and XVI).
Orange-Ochraceous=16 *h* (Plate III).
Orange Vermilion=4, dull (Plate I).
Orpiment Orange=11 *h* (Plate II).
Peach-blossom Pink=1 *e* (Plate I).
Poppy Red: between 3 and 5 *h* (Plate I).
Saffron Yellow=18 (see Plates III and IV).
Saturn Red=11 *a* (Plate II).
Scarlet Vermilion=4, dull (Plate I).
Sevres Blue=46 *h* (Plate VIII).
Solferino=67 *h* (Plate XII).
Tawny-Ochraceous=14' *h* (Plate XV).
Turquoise Blue=44 *b* (Plate XX)
Verditer Blue: Between 43' and 43'' *b* (see Plates XX and XXXIV).
Vermilion: Between 3 and 3' (see Plates I and XIII).
Violet=61 *h* (Plate XI).
Wine Purple=70 *h* (Plate XXVI).

A FEW OF THE MODERN BOOKS ON THE SUBJECT
OF COLOR WHICH THE AUTHOR OF THIS
WORK HAS FOUND MOST USEFUL

Bradley, Milton, author of "Color in the Schoolroom" and "Color in the Kindergarden." — Elementary Color. With an Introduction by Henry Lafavour, Ph. D., Professor of Physics, Williams College. Milton Bradley and Co., Springfield, Mass. [1895]. Small 8vo., pp. [i] - iv, [1] - 128; colored frontispiece ("miniature color charts made from the Bradley educational colored papers," showing 126 unnamed colors) and numerous figures in text.

The present writer frankly and gratefully acknowledges that he has learned more, and learned it more easily, from this little book, which is a model of conciseness and perspicuity, than from careful study of more elaborate and authoritative works on the subject. It is therefore most heartily recommended to the student as a preliminary, at least, to the study of more technical works on color.

Bradley, Milton. — The Evolution of a Practical System of Color Education based on Spectrum Standards. Milton Bradley Co., Springfield, Mass. Pamphlet, 8vo., pp. 8.

Bradley, Milton. — A Few Practical Suggestions relating to Color Standards and the Present Status of Elementary Color Instruction in the United States. Milton Bradley Co., Springfield, Mass. Pamphlet, small 8vo., pp. 16.

Bradley, Milton. — Some Criticisms of Popular Color Definitions, and Suggestions for a Better Color Nomenclature. Milton Bradley Co., Springfield, Mass., 1898. Pamphlet, 12mo., pp. 15.

Bradley, Milton. — The Bradley Color Scheme, with Suggestions to Teachers. Milton Bradley Co., Springfield, Mass. Pamphlet, 12mo., pp. 45.

Church, A. H., F. R. S., etc., Professor of Chemistry in the Royal Academy of Arts in London. — The Chemistry of Paints and Painting. Third edition, revised and enlarged. London: Seeley and Co. Small 8vo., pp. [i-vii] viii-xx, 1-355. An invaluable work which should be consulted by every painter.

Hurst, George H., F. C. S., etc. — Colour: A Handbook of the Theory of Colour. With ten coloured plates and seventy-two illustrations. London: Scott, Greenwood & Co., 1900., 8vo., 160 pp.

Rood, Ogden N. — Students' Text-book of Color; or Modern Chromatics, with applications to Art and Industry. New York: D. Appleton and Company, 1903. Small 8vo., pp. [i-v] vi-viii, [9] 10-329 ; 1 colored plate (frontispiece) and 130 original illustrations.

(One of the best technical works on the physics of color.)

Vanderpoel, Emily Noyes. — Color Problems. A Practical Manual for the Lay Student of Color. With one hundred and seventeen colored plates. Longmans, Green and Co., New York, London and Bombay. 1903. Small 8vo., pp., [i-vi] vii-xv, [1-2] 3-137.

The colored plates of this excellent work illustrate the physics and psychology of color, color harmonies, and kindred subjects, but have no relation to color nomenclature.

Jorgensen, Charles Julius. — The Mastery of Color. A simple and perfect color system, based upon the spectral colors, for educational and practical use in the Arts and Crafts. Published by the Author. Milwaukee, 1906. 8vo., 2 vols., one of text, the other of 22 loose colored plates contained in double box.

An exceedingly useful work for artists and decorators, but not adapted to the needs of science. The technical execution of the plates is exquisite and the colors very fine.

CAUTION!!!

THE pigments used in the preparation of these Plates are the
most durable known, those which have been proven unstable
having been, as far as possible, discarded. The latter include
carmine and other cochineal lakes, colors of vegetable origin
(as gamboge, violet carmine, indigo, etc.), and most of the aniline
or coal tar dyes, though among the last are a considerable number
which are really more permanent than several colors habitually
used by artists. Certain colors in this work could not, however,
possibly be reproduced except by the employment of pigments
which are more or less sensitive to *prolonged exposure* to light,
and hence this caution not to expose the plates unnecessarily.

(See *Church:* "The Chemistry of Paints and Painting," third edition, pages
257-263.)

Plate 1

1. RED	3. O-R.	5. OO-R.
Hermosa Pink	La France Pink	Shrimp Pink
Eosine Pink	*Geranium Pink	Strawberry Pink
Begonia Rose	Rose Doree	Peach Red
Spectrum Red	Scarlet-Red	*Scarlet
*Carmine	Nopal Red	Brazil Red
Ox-blood Red	Garnet Brown	Morocco Red
Victoria Lake	*Maroon	*Claret Brown

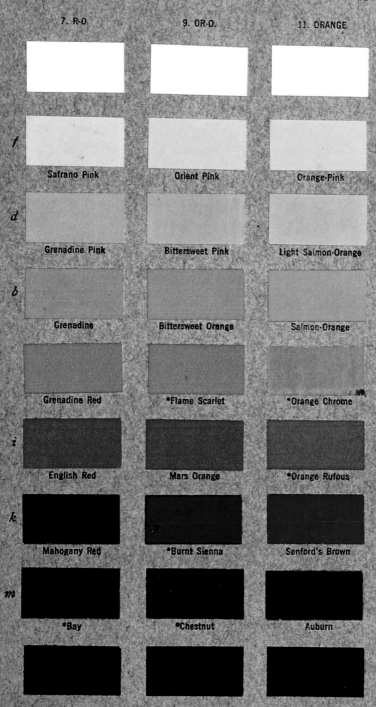

Plate II

7. R-O.   9. OR-O.   11. ORANGE

f

Safrano Pink   Orient Pink   Orange-Pink

d

Grenadine Pink   Bittersweet Pink   Light Salmon-Orange

b

Grenadine   Bittersweet Orange   Salmon-Orange

Grenadine Red   *Flame Scarlet   *Orange Chrome

i

English Red   Mars Orange   *Orange Rufous

k

Mahogany Red   *Burnt Sienna   Sanford's Brown

m

*Bay   *Chestnut   Auburn

13. OY-O.	15. Y-O.	17. O-Y.
f Capucine Buff	Pale Yellow-Orange	Pale Orange-Yellow
d Capucine Orange	*Orange-Buff	Light Orange-Yellow
b Mikado Orange	Capucine Yellow	*Deep Chrome
*Cadmium Orange	*Orange	*Cadmium Yellow
i Xanthine Orange	Mars Yellow	*Raw Sienna
k Amber Brown	Sudan Brown	Antique Brown
m Argus Brown	Brussels Brown	*Raw Umber

Plate IV

| 19. YO-Y. | 21. O-YY. | 23. YELLOW |

f	*Maize Yellow	Baryta Yellow	Martius Yellow
d	*Buff-Yellow	Pinard Yellow	Picric Yellow
b	Apricot Yellow	Empire Yellow.	Pale Lemon Yellow
	Light Cadmium	Lemon Chrome	*Lemon Yellow
i	Aniline Yellow	Sulphine Yellow	Pyrite Yellow
k	Orange-Citrine	Citrine	Warbler Green
m	Medal Bronze	Dark Citrine	*Olive-Green

Plate V

25. YG-Y. 27. G-Y. 29. GG-Y.

t

*Sulphur Yellow Pale Green-Yellow Pale Viridine Yellow

d

Pale Greenish Yellow Light Green-Yellow Light Viridine Yellow

b

Light Greenish Yellow Green-Yellow Viridine Yellow

Greenish Yellow Bright Green-Yellow Neva Green

i

Oil Yellow Javel Green Cosse Green

k

Yellowish Oil Green *Oil Green Lettuce Green

m

Calla Green Cerro Green Spinach Green

Plate VI

31. Y-G.	33. GY-G.	35. GREEN
Pale Yellow-Green	Light Viridine Green	Pale Cendre Green
Light Yellow-Green	Viridine Green	Light Cendre Green
Clear Yellow-Green	Vanderpoel's Green	Cendre Green
Yellow-Green	Night Green	*Emerald Green
Calliste Green	Scheele's Green	Peacock Green
*Parrot Green	*Grass Green	Meadow Green
Cedar Green	Cossack Green	Antique Green

t
d
b
i
k
m

Plate VII

37. GB-G.	39. B-G.	41. BB-G.

t

Opaline Green	Pale Blue-Green	Pale Turquoise Green

d

Neuvider Green	Light Blue-Green	Turquoise Green

b

Chrysoprase Green	Tyrolite Green	Venice Green

Vivid Green	Skobeloff Green	Benzol Green

i

*Viridian Green	Guinea Green	Ethyl Green

k

Dark Viridian Green	Wall Green	Sorrento Green

m

Diamine Green	Anthracene Green	*Myrtle Green

Plate VIII

43. G-B.	45. BG-B.	47. G-BB.

f

| Beryl Blue | *Pale Blue. (Ethyl Blue) | Pallid Methyl Blue |

d

| Calamine Blue | Pale Cerulean Blue | Pale Methyl Blue |

b

| Cendre Blue | Light Cerulean Blue | Light Methyl Blue |

| Italian Blue | *Cerulean Blue | Methyl Blue |

i

| Peacock Blue | Oxide Blue | Leitch's Blue |

k

| Patent Blue | *Antwerp Blue | *Paris Blue |

m

| Blackish Green-Blue | *Marine Blue | *Berlin Blue |

Plate IX

49. BLUE	51. BV-B.	53. V-B.

f

| Pale Mazarine Blue | Pale Amparo Blue | Pallid Violet-Blue |

d

| Mazarine Blue | Light Amparo Blue | Pale Violet-Blue |

b

| Salvia Blue | Amparo Blue | Light Violet-Blue |

| Spectrum Blue | Bradley's Blue | Phenyl Blue |

"i

| *Ultramarine Blue | Lyons Blue | *Smalt Blue |

k

| Rood's Blue | Helvetia Blue | Hay's Blue |

m

| Prussian Blue | *Cyanine Blue | Azurite Blue |

Plate X

	55. B-V.	57. VB-V.	59. VIOLET
f	Pallid Blue-Violet	Pallid Bluish Violet	Pallid Violet
d	Pale Blue-Violet	Pale Bluish Violet	Pale Violet
b	Light Blue-Violet	Light Bluish Violet	Light Violet
	Blue-Violet	Bluish Violet	Spectrum Violet
i	Deep Blue-Violet	Violet Ultramarine	*Royal Purple
k	*Hyacinth Blue	Roslyn Blue	Dark Violet
m	Dark Aniline Blue	Dark Bluish Violet	Blackish Violet

Plate XI

61. VR-V.	63. R-V.	65. RR-V.

f	Pale Hortense Violet	Pale Amparo Purple	Phlox Pink
d	Light Hortense Violet	Light Amparo Purple	Light Phlox Purple
b	Hortense Violet	Amparo Purple	*Phlox Purple
	Amethyst Violet	Violet-Purple	Purple. (True)
i	Hyacinth Violet	Pansy Violet	Rood's Violet
k	Mulberry Purple	Cotinga Purple	Raisin Purple
m	Fluorite Violet	*Prune Purple	Blackish Purple

Plate XII

67. V-R.	69. RV-R.	71. V-RR.

	67. V-R.	69. RV-R.	71. V-RR.
f	Mallow Pink	Pale Amaranth Pink	*Rose Pink
d	Light Mallow Purple	Amaranth Pink	Deep Rose Pink
b	Mallow Purple	Tyrian Pink	Rose Color
	Rhodamine Purple	Tyrian Rose	*Rose Red
i	*Aster Purple	Amaranth Purple	*Pomegranate Purple
k	*Dahlia Purple	*Pansy Purple	Bordeaux
m	Blackish Red-Purple	Violet Carmine	Burnt Lake

Plate XIII

	1′. RED	3′. O-R.	5′. OO-R.
f	Venetian Pink	Chatenay Pink	Flesh-Pink
d	Alizarine Pink	Jasper Pink	Coral Pink
b	Old Rose	Light Jasper Red	Light Coral Red
	Eugenia Red	Jasper Red	*Coral Red
i	Acajou Red	Pompeian Red	*Dragon's-blood Red
k	Vandyke Red	*Madder Brown	*Brick Red
m	Hay's Maroon	Diamine Brown	Hessian Brown

Plate XIV

7'. R-O.	9'. OR-O.	11'. ORANGE

f

| Pale Flesh Color | Pale Salmon Color | Seashell Pink |

d

| *Flesh Color | *Salmon Color | *Salmon-Buff |

b

| Carrot Red | Flesh-Ocher | Apricot Buff |

| Carnelian Red | *Rufous | Apricot Orange |

i

| *Vinaceous-Rufous | *Ferruginous | *Cinnamon-Rufous |

k

| Hay's Russet | Kaiser Brown | *Hazel |

m

| *Liver Brown | Carob Brown | Chestnut-Brown |

Plate XV

13′. OY-O	15′. Y-O.	17′. O-Y.
Pale Ochraceous-Salmon	Pale Ochraceous-Buff	Light Buff
Light Ochraceous-Salmon	Light Ochraceous-Buff	Warm Buff
Ochraceous-Salmon	*Ochraceous-Buff	Antimony Yellow
Zinc Orange	Ochraceous-Orange	Yellow Ocher
*Tawny	Ochraceous-Tawny	Buckthorn Brown
*Russet	Cinnamon-Brown	Dresden Brown
*Mars Brown	*Prout's Brown	*Mummy Brown

f
d
b
i
k
m

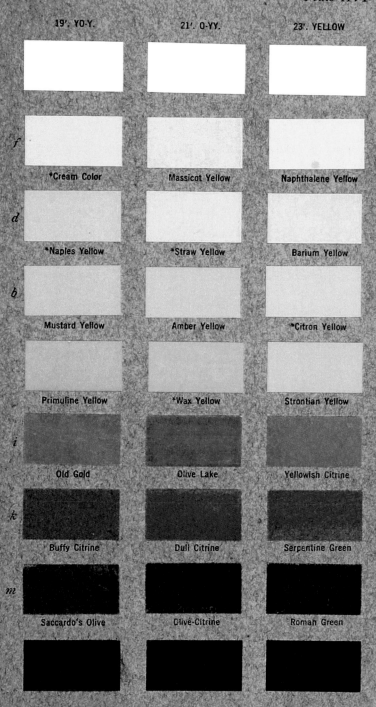

Plate XVI

19'. YO-Y.	21'. O-YY.	23'. YELLOW
*Cream Color	Massicot Yellow	Naphthalene Yellow
*Naples Yellow	*Straw Yellow	Barium Yellow
Mustard Yellow	Amber Yellow	*Citron Yellow
Primuline Yellow	*Wax Yellow	Strontian Yellow
Old Gold	Olive Lake	Yellowish Citrine
Buffy Citrine	Dull Citrine	Serpentine Green
Saccardo's Olive	Olive-Citrine	Roman Green

Plate XVII

25′. YG-Y.	27′. G-Y.	29′. GG-Y.

	25′. YG-Y.	27′. G-Y.	29′. GG-Y.
f	Pale Chalcedony Yellow	Pale Dull Green-Yellow	Pale Lumiere Green
d	Light Chalcedony Yellow	Light Dull Green-Yellow	Light Lumiere Green
b	Chalcedony Yellow	Clear Dull Green-Yellow	Lumiere Green
	Bright Chalcedony Yellow	Dull Green-Yellow	*Apple Green
i	Courge Green	Biscay Green	Light Bice Green
k	Light Hellebore Green	Light Elm Green	*Bice Green
m	Hellebore Green	Elm Green	Forest Green

Plate XVIII

31'. Y-G.	33'. GY-G.	35'. GREEN

t

Pale Veronese Green	Pale Tiber Green	Oural Green

d

Veronese Green	Tiber Green	Light Paris Green

b

Rivage Green	Light Oriental Green	*Paris Green

Mineral Green	Oriental Green	Motmot Green

i

Rinnemann's Green	Winter Green	Killarney Green

k

Civette Green	Hay's Green	Ackermann's Green

m

Varley's Green	Dark Yellowish Green	Dark Green

Plate XIX

37'. GB-G.	39'. B-G.	41'. BB-G.
Dull Opaline Green	Microcline Green	Pale Nile Blue
Variscite Green	Pale Sulphate Green	*Nile Blue
Cobalt Green	Light Sulphate Green	*Beryl Green
*Verdigris Green	Sulphate Green	Methyl Green
Zinc Green	Dark Sulphate Green	*Sea Green
Dark Zinc Green	Dark Cinnabar Green	Prussian Green
*Bottle Green	Duck Green	Invisible Green

f
d
b
i
k
m

Plate XX

	43'. G-B.	45'. BG-B.	47'. G-BB.
f	Etain Blue	Persian Blue	Light Sky Blue
d	Lumiere Blue	Light Squill Blue	Sky Blue
b	Bremen Blue	Squill Blue	Yale Blue
	Motmot Blue	Mathews' Blue	Olympic Blue
i	Capri Blue	*China Blue	Vanderpoel's Blue
k	Jouvence Blue	Chessylite Blue	Blanc's Blue
m	Dusky Green-Blue (1)	Dark Chessylite Blue	Dusky Greenish Blue

Plate XXI

49'. BLUE	51'. BV-B.	53'. V-B.

f

| Pale Grayish Blue | Wedgewood Blue | Light Lavender-Blue |

d

| Pale Cadet Blue | Deep Wedgewood Blue | Lavender-Blue |

b

| Light Cadet Blue | *Flax-flower Blue | Deep Lavender-Blue |

| Clear Cadet Blue | Commelina Blue | Cornflower Blue |

i

| Cadet Blue | Diva Blue | Gentian Blue |

k

| Deep Cadet Blue | Dark Diva Blue | Sailor Blue |

m

| Dark Cadet Blue | Alizarine Blue | Navy Blue |

Plate XXII

47*. IG-BB.	49*. BLUE	51*. BV-B.
Pale King's Blue	Pale Neropalin Blue	Pale Forget-me-not Blue
Light King's Blue	Light Neropalin Blue	Light Forget-me-not Blue
King's Blue	Neropalin Blue	Forget-me-not Blue
Venetian Blue	Ultramarine Ash	Dull Violaceous Blue
Jay Blue	Chapman's Blue	Grayish Violaceous Blue
Gendarme Blue	Eton Blue	Deep Dull Violaceous Blue
Hortense Blue	Dusky Blue	Indulin Blue

f, *d*, *b*, *i*, *k*, *m*

Plate XXIII

55′. B-V.	57′. VB-V.	59′. VIOLET

f

| Pallid Soft Blue-Violet | Pale Wistaria Blue | Pale Wistaria Violet |

d

| Pale Soft Blue-Violet | Light Wistaria Blue | Light Wistaria Violet |

b

| Light Soft Blue-Violet | Wistaria Blue | Wistaria Violet |

| Soft Blue-Violet | Soft Bluish Violet | Bradley's Violet |

i

| Deep Soft Blue-Violet | Deep Soft Bluish Violet | Dauphin's Violet |

k

| Dark Soft Blue-Violet | Dark Soft Bluish Violet | Blanc's Violet |

m

| Dusky Violet-Blue (1) | Dusky Blue-Violet (1) | Dusky Violet |

Plate XXIV

53*. V-B.	55*. B-V.	57*. VB-V.

f

Pallid Grayish Violet-Blue	Pale Campanula Blue	Light Chicory Blue

d

Pale Grayish Violet-Blue	Light Campanula Blue	Chicory Blue

b

Light Grayish Violet-Blue	*Campanula Blue	Deep Chicory Blue

Dull Violet-Blue	Dull Blue-Violet (1)	Dull Bluish Violet (1)

i

Grayish Violet-Blue	Grayish Blue-Violet (1)	Deep Dull Bluish Violet (1)

k

Dark Dull Violet-Blue	Dark Grayish Blue-Violet	Dark Dull Bluish Violet (1)

m

Urania Blue	Dusky Blue-Violet (2)	*Plum Purple

Plate XXV

61'. VR-V.	63'. R-V	65'. RR-V.
Pale Lavender-Violet	Pale Mauve	Mauvette
Light Lavender-Violet	Light Mauve	*Lilac
Lavender-Violet	*Mauve	Chinese Violet
Pleroma Violet	Manganese Violet	Mathews' Purple
Haematoxylin Violet	Litho Purple	Petunia Violet
Anthracene Violet	Madder Violet	Nigrosin Violet
Dark Anthracene Violet	Dark Madder Violet	Dark Nigrosin Violet

f
d
b
i
k
m

Plate XXVI

67'. V-R.   69'. RV-R.   71'. V-RR.

f

Pale Rose-Purple   Rosolane Pink   Cameo Pink

d

*Rose-Purple   Pale Rosolane Purple   Thulite Pink

b

Liseran Purple   Light Rosolane Purple   Spinel Pink

*Magenta   Rosolane Purple   Spinel Red

i

Dull Magenta Purple   Schoenfeld's Purple   Indian Lake

k

Dull Dark Purple   *Auricula Purple   Dahlia Carmine

m

Dull Dusky Purple   Dusky Auricula Purple   Dark Maroon-Purple

Plate XXVII

1″. RED	3″. O-R.	5″. OO-R.
Pale Vinaceous	Livid Pink	Hydrangea Pink
*Vinaceous	Corinthian Pink	Pinkish Vinaceous
Deep Vinaceous	Light Corinthian Red	Orange-Vinaceous
Dark Vinaceous	Corinthian Red	Etruscan Red
Hydrangea Red	Deep Corinthian Red	Ocher Red
Mineral Red	Indian Red	Prussian Red
Dark Mineral Red	Dark Indian Red	Haematite Red

f

d

b

i

k

m

Plate XXVIII

7". R-O.	9". OR-O.	11". ORANGE

f

Pale Congo Pink	Pale Vinaceous-Pink	Shell Pink

d

Light Congo Pink	*Vinaceous-Pink	*Buff-Pink

b

Congo Pink	Japan Rose	Onion-skin Pink

Terra Cotta	Testaceous	Vinaceous-Tawny

i

Vinaceous-Russet	Cacao Brown	Pecan Brown

k

Cameo Brown	*Walnut Brown	Rood's Brown

m

*Chocolate	*Burnt Umber	*Vandyke Brown

Plate XXIX

13′′. OY-O.	15′′. Y-O.	17′′. O-Y.

f
| Pale Cinnamon-Pink | Pale Pinkish Cinnamon | Pale Pinkish Buff |

d
| Light Vinaceous-Cinnamon | Light Pinkish Cinnamon | *Pinkish Buff |

b
| *Vinaceous-Cinnamon | Pinkish Cinnamon | Cinnamon-Buff |

| Orange-Cinnamon | *Cinnamon | *Clay Color |

i
| Mikado Brown | Sayal Brown | *Tawny-Olive |

k
| Verona Brown | Snuff Brown | Saccardo's Umber |

m
| Warm Sepia | *Bister | *Sepia |

Plate XXX

	19″. YO-Y.	21″. O-YY.	23″. YELLOW
f	Cartridge Buff	Ivory Yellow	Marguerite Yellow
d	Cream-Buff	Colonial Buff	*Primrose Yellow
b	Chamois	Deep Colonial Buff	Reed Yellow
	Honey Yellow	Olive-Ocher	*Olive-Yellow
i	Isabella Color	Ecru-Olive	Light Yellowish Olive
k	Light Brownish Olive	Buffy Olive	Yellowish Olive
m	Brownish Olive	*Olive	Dark Greenish Olive

Plate XXXI

25″. YG-Y.	27″. G-Y.	29″. GG-Y.

_f_

| Sea-foam Yellow | Sea-foam Green | Pale Glass Green |

_d_

| Chartreuse Yellow | Deep Sea-foam Green | Glass Green |

_b_

| Citron Green | Chrysolite Green | Kildare Green |

| Lime Green | Deep Chrysolite Green | Absinthe Green |

_i_

| Mignonette Green | Rainette Green | Light Cress Green |

_k_

| Krönberg's Green | Jade Green | Cress Green |

_m_

| Ivy Green | Yew Green | Dark Cress Green |

Plate XXXII

31''. Y-G.	33''. GY-G.	35''. GREEN
Pale Turtle Green	Pale Fluorite Green	Pale Olivine
Light Turtle Green	Light Fluorite Green	Olivine
Turtle Green	Clear Fluorite Green	*Malachite Green
Deep Turtle Green	Fluorite Green	Deep Malachite Green
*Chromium Green	Shamrock Green	*French Green
Deep Dull Yellow-Green (1)	Deep Dull Yellow-Green (2)	Light Danube Green
Dark Dull Yellow-Green	Empire Green	Danube Green

f

d

b

i

k

m

Plate XXXIII

37″. GB-G.	39″. B-G.	41″. BB-G.

f

| Lichen Green | Pale Glaucous-Green | Pale Niagara Green |

d

| Deep Lichen Green | *Glaucous-Green | Light Niagara Green |

b

| Rejane Green | Deep Glaucous-Green | Niagara Green |

| Montpellier Green | Light Porcelain Green | Light Terre Verte |

i

| Jasper Green | Porcelain Green | *Terre Verte |

k

| Nickel Green | Dark Porcelain Green | Dark Terre Verte |

m

| Dusky Green | Dusky Blue-Green | Dusky Bluish Green |

Plate XXXIV

43″. G-B.	45″. BG-B.	47″. G-BB.
t Pale Glaucous-Blue	Sky Gray.	Burn Blue
d Light Glaucous-Blue	Light Alice Blue	Light Columbia Blue
b *Glaucous-Blue	Alice Blue	Columbia Blue
Porcelain Blue	Orient Blue	Light Tyrian Blue
i Gobelin Blue	Deep Orient Blue	Tyrian Blue
k Dark Gobelin Blue	Dark Orient Blue	Dark Tyrian Blue
m Dusky Green Blue (2)	Dusky Orient Blue	*Indigo Blue

49″. BLUE	51″. BV-B.	53″. V-B.
*Pearl Blue	Pale Grayish Blue-Violet	Pale Aniline Lilac
Pale Windsor Blue	Light Grayish Blue-Violet	Aniline Lilac
Light Windsor Blue	Grayish Blue-Violet (2)	Deep Aniline Lilac
Clear Windsor Blue	Dull Bluish Violet (2)	Dull Violet-Blue
Windsor Blue	Deep Dull Bluish Violet (2)	Deep Dull Violet-Blue
Acetin Blue	Dark Dull Bluish Violet (2)	Dark Dull Violet-Blue
Nigrosin Blue	Diamin-Azo Blue	Dusky Dull Violet-Blue

Plate XXXVI

	55″. B-V.	57″. VB-V.	59″. VIOLET
f	Pale Verbena Violet	Pale Bluish Lavender	*Lavender
d	Verbena Violet	Bluish Lavender	Deep Lavender
b	Ontario Violet	Light Dull Bluish Violet	Light Hyssop Violet
	Vanderpoel's Violet	Dull Bluish Violet (3)	Hyssop Violet
i	Dull Blue-Violet (2)	Deep Dull Bluish Violet (3)	Deep Hyssop Violet
k	Yvette Violet	Dark Dull Bluish Violet (3)	Dark Hyssop Violet
m	Dark Yvette Violet	Dusky Dull Violet (1)	Dusky Dull Violet (2)

Plate XXXVII

61″. VR-V.	63″. R-V.	65″. RR-V.
Pale Lobelia Violet	Pale Lilac	Light Pinkish Lilac
Light Lobelia Violet	Hay's Lilac	Purplish Lilac
Lobelia Violet	Ageratum Violet	Argyle Purple
Saccardo's Violet	Aconite Violet	Bishop's Purple
Livid Violet	Livid Purple	Light Perilla Purple
Naphthalene Violet	Deep Livid Purple	Perilla Purple
Dark Naphthalene Violet	Dark Livid Purple	Dark Perilla Purple

f *d* *b* *i* *k* *m*

Plate XXXVIII

67''. V-R.   69''. RV-R.   71''. V-RR.

f

Pale Laelia Pink   Pale Persian Lilac   Pale Rhodonite Pink

d

Laelia Pink   Persian Lilac   Rhodonite Pink

b

Tourmaline Pink   Daphne Pink   Rocellin Purple

Eupatorium Purple   Daphne Red   Hellebore Red

i

Vinaceous-Purple   Vernonia Purple   Deep Hellebore Red

k

Dark Vinaceous-Purple   Corinthian Purple   Neutral Red

m

*Indian Purple   Dark Corinthian Purple   Mars Violet

Plate XXXIX

1'''. RED	5'''. OO-R.	9'''. OR-O.
Pale Purplish Vinaceous	Pale Brownish Vinaceous	Pale Grayish Vinaceous
Light Purplish Vinaceous	Light Brownish Vinaceous	Light Grayish Vinaceous
Purplish Vinaceous	Brownish Vinaceous	Light Russet-Vinaceous
Livid Brown	Deep Brownish Vinaceous	Russet-Vinaceous
Deep Livid Brown	Vinaceous-Brown	Sorghum Brown
Dark Livid Brown	Dark Vinaceous-Brown	Hay's Brown
Warm Blackish Brown	*Seal Brown	Light Seal Brown

f
d
b
i
k
m

Plate XL

13'''. OY-O.	17'''. O-Y.	21'''. O-YY.
f Pale Vinaceous-Fawn	Tilleul-Buff	Pale Olive-Buff
d Light Vinaceous-Fawn	*Vinaceous-Buff	*Olive-Buff
b Vinaceous-Fawn	Avellaneous	Deep Olive-Buff
*Fawn Color	*Wood Brown	Dark Olive-Buff
i Army Brown	Buffy Brown	Citrine-Drab
k Natal Brown	Olive-Brown	Deep Olive
m Bone Brown	*Clove Brown	Dark Olive

Plate XLI

25′′′. YG-Y.	29′′′. GG-Y.	33′′′. GY-G.
Yellowish Glaucous	Glaucous	Greenish Glaucous
Water Green	Corydalis Green	Deep Greenish Glaucous
Light Grape Green	Mytho Green	Dark Greenish Glaucous
Grape Green	Asphodel Green	Pistachio Green
Deep Grape Green	Pois Green	American Green
Lincoln Green	Leaf Green	Dark American Green
Dusky Olive-Green	Dusky Yellowish Green	Dull Blackish Green

Plate XLII

37'''. GB-G.	41'''. BB-G.	45'''. BG-B.

f

Bluish Glaucous | Pale Dull Glaucous-Blue | Pale Russian Blue

d

Deep Bluish Glaucous | Light Dull Glaucous-Blue | Russian Blue

b

Dark Bluish Glaucous | Greenish Glaucous-Blue | Cadet Gray

Stone Green | Bluish Gray-Green | Parula Blue

i

Russian Green | Deep Bluish Gray-Green | Delft Blue

k

Dark Russian Green | Dark Bluish Gray-Green | Deep Delft Blue

m

Dusky Dull Green | Dusky Dull Bluish Green | Dark Delft Blue

Plate XLIII

	49'''. BLUE	53'''. V-B.	57'''. VB-V.
f	*Lavender Gray	Plumbago Blue	Grayish Lavender
d	Endive Blue	Deep Plumbago Blue	Deep Grayish Lavender
b	Dutch Blue	Dark Plumbago Blue	Dark Grayish Lavender
	Deep Dutch Blue	Madder Blue	Ramier Blue
i	Slate-Blue	Deep Madder Blue	Slate-Violet (1)
k	Deep Slate-Blue	Dark Madder Blue	Dark Slate-Violet (1)
m	Dusky Slate-Blue	Dusky Violet-Blue (2)	Dusky Slate-Violet

Plate XLIV

	61'''. VR-V.	65'''. RR-V.	69'''. RV-R.
f	Dull Lavender	Vinaceous-Lavender	Pale Vinaceous-Lilac
d	Deep Dull Lavender	Deep Vinaceous-Lavender	Light Vinaceous-Lilac
b	Dark Lavender	Light Vinaceous-Purple	Vinaceous-Lilac
	Slate-Violet (2)	Vinaceous-Purple	Deep Purplish Vinaceous
i	Deep Slate-Violet	Slate-Purple	Dull Indian Purple
k	Dark Slate-Violet (2)	Dark Slate-Purple	Anthracene Purple
m	Dull Violet-Black (1)	Raisin Black	Taupe Brown

Plate XLV

1′′′′. RED	5′′′′. OO-R.	9′′′′. OR-O.

t

| Pallid Purple-Drab | Pallid Vinaceous-Drab | Pallid Brownish Drab |

d

| Pale Purple-Drab | Pale Vinaceous-Drab | Pale Brownish Drab |

b

| Light Purple-Drab | Light Vinaceous-Drab | Light Brownish Drab |

| Purple-Drab | Vinaceous-Drab | Brownish Drab |

i

| Dark Purple-Drab | Dark Vinaceous-Drab | Deep Brownish Drab |

k

| Dusky Brown | Dark Grayish Brown | Dusky Drab |

m

| Blackish Brown (1) | Blackish Brown (2) | Blackish Brown (3) |

Plate XLVI

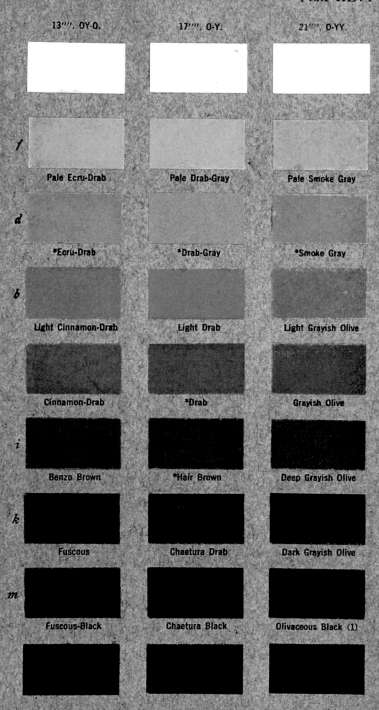

13″″. OY-O.   17″″. O-Y.   21″″. O-YY.

f

Pale Ecru-Drab   Pale Drab-Gray   Pale Smoke Gray

d

*Ecru-Drab   *Drab-Gray   *Smoke Gray

b

Light Cinnamon-Drab   Light Drab   Light Grayish Olive

Cinnamon-Drab   *Drab   Grayish Olive

i

Benzo Brown   *Hair Brown   Deep Grayish Olive

k

Fuscous   Chaetura Drab   Dark Grayish Olive

m

Fuscous-Black   Chaetura Black   Olivaceous Black (1)

Plate XLVII

25''''. YG-Y.	29''''. GG-Y.	33''''. GY-G.

f

| Light Mineral Gray | Court Gray | Puritan Gray |

d

| Mineral Gray | Gnaphalium Green | Light Celandine Green |

b

| Tea Green | *Pea Green | Celandine Green |

| Vetiver Green | *Sage Green | Artemisia Green |

i

| Andover Green | Slate-Olive | Lily Green |

k

| Dark Ivy Green | Deep Slate-Olive | Deep Slate-Green |

m

| Olivaceous Black (2) | Dull Greenish Black (1) | Dull Greenish Black (2) |

Plate XLVIII

37''''. GB-G.   41''''. BB-G.   45''''. BG-B.

f

Glaucous-Gray   Pale Medici Blue   Pale Green-Blue Gray

d

Deep Glaucous-Gray   Light Medici Blue   Clear Green-Blue Gray

b

Dark Glaucous-Gray   Medici Blue   Deep Green-Blue Gray

Grayish Blue-Green   Deep Medici Blue   Dark Green-Blue Gray

i

Deep Grayish Blue-Green   Dark Medici Blue   Green-Blue Slate

k

Dark Grayish Blue-Green   Saccardo's Slate   Dark Green-Blue Slate

m

Greenish Slate-Black   Dull Blue-Green Black   Bluish Slate-Black

Plate XLIX

49''''. BLUE	53''''. V·B.	57''''. VB·V.

f

Pale Payne's Gray	Pale Violet-Plumbeous	Rood's Lavender

d

Light Payne's Gray	Light Violet-Plumbeous	Pale Varley's Gray

b

Clear Payne's Gray	Violet-Plumbeous	Light Varley's Gray

Payne's Gray	Deep Violet-Plumbeous	Varley's Gray

i

Deep Payne's Gray	Violet-Slate	Deep Varley's Gray

k

Dark Payne's Gray	Dark Violet-Slate	Dark Varley's Gray

m

Bluish Black	Dull Violet-Black (2)	Blue-Violet Black

Plate L

61''''. VR-V.	65''''. RR-V.	69'''. RV-R.
f Light Plumbago Gray	Light Heliotrope Gray	Light Vinaceous-Gray
d Plumbago Gray	Heliotrope Gray	Vinaceous-Gray
b Deep Plumbago Gray	Deep Heliotrope Gray	Deep Vinaceous-Gray
Dark Plumbago Gray	Dark Heliotrope Gray	Dark Vinaceous-Gray
i Plumbago-Slate	Heliotrope-Slate	Vinaceous-Slate
k Dark Plumbago-Slate	Dark Heliotrope-Slate	Deep Slaty Brown
m Dull Violet-Black	Dull Purplish Black	Aniline Black

Plate LI

1″″. RED	15″″. Y-O.	23″″. YELLOW

ƒ

Pallid Quaker Drab	Pallid Mouse Gray	Pale Olive-Gray

d

Pale Quaker Drab	Pale Mouse Gray	Light Olive-Gray

b

Light Quaker Drab	Light Mouse Gray	*Olive-Gray

Quaker Drab	*Mouse Gray	Deep Olive-Gray

i

Deep Quaker Drab	Deep Mouse Gray	Dark Olive-Gray

k

Dark Quaker Drab	Dark Mouse Gray	Iron Gray

m

Sooty Black	Blackish Mouse Gray	Olivaceous Black (3)

Plate LII

35′′′′′. GREEN   49′′′′′. BLUE   59′′′′′. VIOLET

	GREEN	BLUE	VIOLET
f	*Pearl Gray	*French Gray	*Lilac Gray
d	Dawn Gray	*Cinereous	Pale Violet-Gray
b	Hathi Gray	*Plumbeous	Light Violet-Gray
	Storm Gray	Deep Plumbeous	Violet-Gray
i	Castor Gray	Dark Plumbeous	Deep Violet-Gray
k	Dusky Green-Gray	Blackish Plumbeous	Dark Violet-Gray
m	Blackish Green-Gray	Plumbeous-Black	Blackish Violet-Gray

Plate. LIII

67''''. V-R.	NEUTRAL GRAY	CARBON GRAY
- White	White	*10. Gray. (Pale Gull Gray)
Pallid Purplish Gray	Pallid Neutral Gray	*9. Gray. (Light Gull Gray)
Pale Purplish Gray	Pale Neutral Gray	*8. Gray. (Gull Gray)
Light Purplish Gray	Light Neutral Gray	*7. Gray. (Deep Gull Gray)
Purplish Gray	Neutral Gray	*6. Gray. (Dark Gull Gray)
Deep Purplish Gray	Deep Neutral Gray	*5. Slate-Gray
Dark Purplish Gray	Dark Neutral Gray	*4. Slate Color
Dusky Purplish Gray	Dusky Neutral Gray	*3. Blackish Slate
Black	*1. Black	*2. Slate-Black

f
d
b
i
k
m